STAR MATHS PUZZLES & PROBLEMS

A fresh approach to using and applying maths

TERMS AND CONDITIONS

IMPORTANT – PERMITTED USE AND WARNINGS – READ CAREFULLY BEFORE USING

Minimum specification:
- PC or Mac with a CD-ROM drive and at least 128 Mb RAM
- Recommended screen resolution: 1280 × 1024 pixels. (See CD help notes for details.)
- Facilities for printing

PC:
- Windows 98SE or above
- Recommended minimum processor speed: 600 MHz

Mac:
- Mac OSX1. or above
- Recommended minimum processor speed: 500 MHz

For all technical support queries, please phone Scholastic Customer Services on 0845 6039091.

Anthony David and Julie Cogill

Authors
Anthony David and Julie Cogill

Development Editor
Niamh O'Carroll

Editor
Helen Kelly

Assistant Editor
Margaret Eaton

Illustrations
Pages 12–31 & 45 © Wizzmedia

Pages 34, 35, 37, 38, 40 & 43 © Rupert van Wyk / Beehive Illustration

Pages 6, 8, 9 & 10 © Blake Publishing / Pascal Press, originally published in *Targeting Maths Problem Solving Level 2* (Pascal Press, 2007)

Series Designer
Joy Monkhouse

Designer
Melissa Leeke

Text © 2008 Anthony David and Julie Cogill
© 2008 Scholastic Ltd

CD-ROM design and development in association with Wizzmedia

Designed using Adobe CS

Published by Scholastic Ltd
Villiers House, Clarendon Avenue,
Leamington Spa, Warwickshire CV32 5PR
www.scholastic.co.uk

Printed by Tien Wah, Singapore
1 2 3 4 5 6 7 8 9   8 9 0 1 2 3 4 5 6 7

ISBN 978-1407-10036-4

ACKNOWLEDGEMENTS
Extracts from the Primary National Strategy's *Primary Framework for Mathematics* (2006) www.standards.dfes.gov.uk/primaryframework © Crown copyright. Reproduced under the terms of the Click Use Licence.

The approved SMART Software Accreditation logo is a trademark of SMART Technologies.

Every effort has been made to trace copyright holders for the works reproduced in this book, and the publishers apologise for any inadvertent omissions.

British Library Cataloguing-in-Publication Data
A catalogue record for this book is available from the British Library.

Introduction

Children need to learn how to solve problems by using and applying mathematics in a variety of contexts. However, when the *Framework for teaching mathematics from Reception to Year 6* was published in 1999, the focus was very much on number and calculations. The 1999 Framework has objectives under the broad heading of 'Solving problems', sub-divided into three sections:

- Making decisions
- Reasoning and generalising about numbers and shapes
- Problems involving 'real life', money or measures

At this point the National Curriculum gave much more attention to 'Using and applying mathematics', building it into all of the mathematics attainment targets. One of the principal aims of the renewed Primary Framework in 2006 therefore was to give greater attention to using and applying mathematics through the five themes of:

- Solving problems
- Representing
- Enquiring
- Reasoning
- Communicating

Star Maths Puzzles and Problems is designed to provide opportunities for children to use and apply mathematics in line with these themes and objectives. Each title reflects progression within the five themes by providing problems that encompass the full range of problem-solving processes and skills. The ten interactive problems on the CD-ROM will involve children in reasoning and predicting outcomes, in communicating their results, and in solving problems and developing lines of enquiry. Additionally, they provide opportunities for children to use problem-solving strategies to help them investigate and understand the mathematical content of each problem. What's more, the activities are engaging and challenging for all ability levels and most can be used flexibly either with the whole class on an interactive whiteboard or in small groups working at a computer.

About the book

Each book includes a set of teachers' notes linked to the interactive activities on the CD-ROM. A range of additional support is also provided, including an introduction to problem-solving strategies such as 'logical reasoning', an objectives grid, follow-up problems linked to the CD-ROM activities and a 'problems bank' designed to consolidate or assess children's grasp of each problem solving strategy.

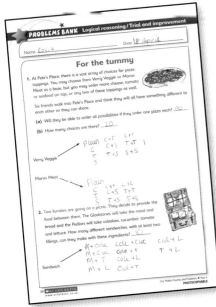

Strategies for using and applying

This book focuses on seven of the key strategies used in mathematical problem solving. Understanding these strategies will greatly assist children in making decisions about how to solve a problem, in organising and interpreting information and results and ultimately in finding solutions to problems. The strategies covered in this book include:

- Work backwards
- Logical reasoning
- Read, plan, work, check
- Trial and improvement
- Make a list
- Act it out
- Look for patterns

This section offers a rationale for each strategy, as well as issues to consider when children are starting to learn different strategies.

Teachers' notes

The teachers' notes cover the ten interactive activities on the CD-ROM. Each page of teachers' notes includes:

Learning objectives
Cover the strands and objectives of the renewed *Primary Framework for Mathematics* (2006) (using and applying objectives as well as objectives from other strands).

Problem-solving strategies
Suggestions for particular strategies to use to solve each CD-ROM problem.

Setting the scene
Setting the context of the problem and instructions for presenting the CD-ROM activity to the children.

Solving the problem
Notes on how to use a particular strategy to solve the CD-ROM problem.

Key questions
Probing questions to be used during the activity, sub-divided by the five themes of using and applying mathematics (see page 4 for further information).

Differentiation
Adapting the activity for more or less confident learners.

Follow up
Getting the children together to consolidate the learning, using practical activities and the related 'follow-up problems' activity sheets.

Problems bank
References to problems bank sheets (see below).

Annotations
At-a-glance instructions for using the CD-ROM activity.

Problems bank

For children to be able to find solutions in unfamiliar situations, they need to have experienced a wide variety of problems and puzzles and be able to call upon a bank of strategies with which to solve them. The 'problems bank' offers a range of problems designed to develop children's understanding of puzzles and problems and build up their use of strategies to solve them. The grid on pages 32–33 breaks down each problem by strategy or objective to help you to select appropriate problems.

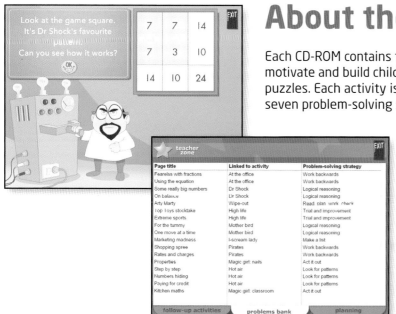

About the CD-ROM

Each CD-ROM contains ten inspiring interactive activities designed to motivate and build children's confidence in solving maths problems and puzzles. Each activity is also designed to practise and reinforce one of the seven problem-solving strategies identified on pages 6–10. The problems are multi-faceted so that the children can return to them over and over again.

The CD-ROM also includes a Teacher zone containing editable objective grids, planning grids and printable versions of the follow-up problems and 'problems bank' activity sheets. Some additional 'problems bank' activities have also been supplied for further support and reinforcement.

Page title	Linked to activity	Problem-solving strategy
Fearless with fractions	At the office	Work backwards
Using the equation	At the office	Work backwards
Some really big numbers	Dr Shock	Logical reasoning
On balance	Dr Shock	Logical reasoning
Arty Marty	Wipe-out	Read, plan, work, check
Top Toys stocktake	High life	Trial and improvement
Extreme sports	High life	Trial and improvement
For the tummy	Mother bird	Logical reasoning
One move at a time	Mother bird	Logical reasoning
Marketing madness	I-scream lady	Make a list
Shopping spree	Pirates	Work backwards
Rates and charges	Pirates	Work backwards
Properties	Magic girl: nails	Act it out
Step by step	Hot air	Look for patterns
Numbers hiding	Hot air	Look for patterns
Paying for credit	Hot air	Look for patterns
Kitchen maths	Magic girl: classroom	Act it out

follow-up activities   problems bank   planning

Work backwards

Rationale

This method is useful when information is given about the end result, but the initial or intermediate information is not known.

Teaching the strategy

Knowledge of inverse operations is necessary, as the term 'working backwards' implies working in the opposite direction. Carefully read all the information given and work through the problem, focusing on the following skills:

1. **Determine which data is the given or certain piece of information**
   Discuss which data is the answer at the end - the final result. Highlight this information.

2. **Determine which is the unknown piece of information**

3. **Determine other data to be used**
   Discuss and highlight the information that has been found.

4. **Estimate**
   Children should be able to see whether the answer will be larger or smaller than the given information.

5. **Use diagrams or equations to set out working**
   - Using the diagram method: The working is drawn up using the pieces of data and the signs of the processes (for example, addition or subtraction).

?	+12	-6	-8	=30

   - Using the equation method: Write an equation from the given data, using a letter or a symbol for the unknown.

6. **Use inverse operations**
   Solve the equation by writing its inverse. For example:
   $U + 19 - 6 \times 3 = 1$; *therefore* $U = 1 + 18 - 19$; $U = 0$.

7. **Check**
   Ask the children to test the solution by reading the problem and substituting data for the unknowns initially used.

8. **Explain**
   Ask children to explain why their calculation is correct. Can they tell you how it meets the criteria in the original problem?

Links to

At the office
pages 12-13

Pirates
pages 24-25

Logical reasoning

Rationale

In using 'logical reasoning' to solve problems, children consider many pieces of information and decide on a systematic method of utilising this information. This involves deciding which piece comes first, 'what is not' as well as 'what is', and how to reach the solution step by step.

Teaching the strategy

There are a number of strategies which come under the umbrella of solving problems by 'logical reasoning'. These include drawing a grid or a matrix, using a diagram, and considering all the information. Chiefly, the children must understand what they are being asked, what information is to be used and in what order it should be utilised.

1. **Read the problem with understanding**
   Highlight the actual question. This is the most important step, as the question and the data often contain tricks or twists that can confuse children.

2. **Decide on the data to be used**
   Decide what is known and what needs to be found out. Use a highlighter, leaving out unnecessary words.

3. **Decide on the strategy to be used**
   ● Draw a grid or matrix and utilise a system to mark 'what is' and 'what is not'.
   ● Use a diagram to position information so that it can be more easily understood.
   ● Make a list. This strategy will simplify the data in the problem so that it can be seen more concisely. Consider all known information about the problem.

4. **Written work**
   Apply the strategy. The strategies all require some writing down of information. Insist that the children write down their working and can communicate this when asked to.

Links to

Dr Shock
pages 14–15

Mother bird
pages 20–21

Magic girl: nails
pages 26–27

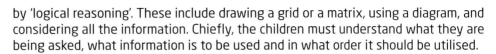

Read, plan, work, check

Rationale
Learning how to structure an investigation is an integral part of developing mathematical thinking. The 'read, plan, work, check' strategy involves understanding and clarifying the question, selecting and using a strategy to solve the problem, working out a solution and checking the solution in terms of the original question. The use of this strategy can lay a firm foundation in children's development of problem-solving skills.

Teaching the strategy
Refer to each of the following steps as you work through the problem with the children.

1. **Read the problem with understanding**
   Carefully read the problem and assimilate the information given. Highlight or underline important words, including the actual question. Ask: *What do you have to find out? What facts will help you to answer the question?*

2. **Make a plan**
   Encourage the children to think carefully about what they need to do in order to solve the problem. Ask: *What are the different steps to this problem? What operations will you need to use?* Invite some children to tell the class how they plan to solve the problem.

3. **Work out the problem**
   Explain that all working out should be left in place as a record of the solution process. Children often think that their working out should be dispensed with if it is incorrect, but you should emphasise that in problem solving the *way* in which a solution is achieved is important.

Links to

Wipe-out
pages 16–17

4. **Check the answer**
   Encourage the children to re-read the problem and check it against their solutions. Pose a variety of other problems that allow them to practise this strategy.

Trial and improvement

Rationale

In using 'trial and improvement' as a problem-solving strategy, children must be able to hazard a good guess. This strategy builds their understanding and confidence. It gives them a starting point when they can't find any other way to start finding a solution.

Teaching the strategy

Use 'trial and improvement' when there is no starting point in the information given. Children need to be able to make good estimates to use this strategy. They also need to understand how to check against the original information given.

1. Determine which information is to be used
Ask the children to carefully read and assimilate the information given in the problem. Rule out any unnecessary information.

2. Highlight important data
Discuss which information is to be used when determining an estimate.

3. Estimate
This is a very important skill. Children must have a feel for where their answers will lie. Large numbers or small? Will it be more or less than any information in the problem text? Ask the children what is reasonable.

4. Check
Test the estimate against the information in the problem. If the need is to add the estimates, will the children reach the correct total? Checking is most important and must be seen to be part of the solution.

5. Adjust up or down
When the first estimate proves to be incorrect, discuss how to determine whether estimates need to be larger or smaller. What information helps make these decisions? Guide children through the selection of second estimates, encouraging them to read the problem again.

6. Working out
Insist that all working out is left in place as a record of the children's thinking. In problem-solving exercises it is important to see how the process progressed. Give part marks for incorrect answers if working out is in place.

7. Explain
Ask children to explain how they arrived at their estimates and how they solved the problem.

Links to

High life
pages 18-19

Mother bird
pages 20-21

Make a list

Rationale

Setting out information in an orderly fashion guides children to think and work systematically. When a list is made, a pattern will often emerge and the solution may come more easily if this is pointed out. Making a list is therefore a step towards finding a pattern to solve similar problems in the future.

Teaching the strategy

Whenever a strategy is not obvious, making a list is a way to see what the information is saying. Also, when all possibilities need to be recorded and counted we make a list.

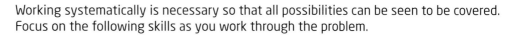

Working systematically is necessary so that all possibilities can be seen to be covered. Focus on the following skills as you work through the problem.

1. Work systematically
Children must be able to decide on a starting point, then work systematically through each item, exhausting all possibilities for that item before moving on to another piece of information. For example, to answer the question 'How many three-digit numbers can be made with the digits 345?' they should start with the 3 in the hundreds position, then 45, followed by 54. Then use 4 in the hundreds, followed by 35, then 53. Lastly, begin with the 5 in the hundreds place, followed by 43, then 34.

2. Physically set out the list
Children will realise that they need space for the list to expand down the page. In some situations, extra paper may need to be supplied. Teachers should introduce scaffolds if required.

3. Visualise/estimate
Children need to visualise possibilities, then they will have a good idea when they have covered them all.

4. Recognise repeat combinations
Ensure that the children understand that there will be repeats, which are not included unless the problem requires it. For example, A with B is the same as B with A, except where the order of the items makes a difference in the combination and should therefore be included.

5. Create a table
Lists may be made into tables, especially where more confident learners are ready to recognise this step. Unlike lists, a table has more than one column, with a heading for each column.

Links to

I-scream lady
pages 22-23

Act it out

Rationale
'Act it out' is similar to 'draw a diagram' in some ways, but it involves the use of objects to clarify the solving of the problem. The use of objects makes it easy to move data around without committing pencil to paper and needing to erase or start again. Being active also makes children more likely to remember the process used, and then be able to use it again.

Teaching the strategy
When choosing suitable objects to use, consider the following:
- Squared paper - when designs, regular layouts, areas or perimeters are involved.
- Coloured pencils - when data needs to be shown differentially.
- Cubes - are usually part of the given data of the problem.
- Cards - when small pieces of paper need to be moved about separately.
- Measuring equipment - when experimentation with various sizes is necessary.
- Water, sand - often used in measuring mass and volume.
- String - when length is part of the data.

The main skills required to successfully utilise this strategy are as follows:

1. Ability to read instructions carefully
Be sure to explain what is required in tasks that have complex instructions. The rules must be followed fully.

Links to

Magic girl: nails
pages 26-27

Magic girl: classroom
pages 30-31

2. **Ability to demonstrate the solution**
   Children need to be able to demonstrate and/or explain their solution as they will have no evidence of the different moves they have made with concrete objects.

3. **Perseverance**
   For some children this is a real issue as many only want to finish quickly with a solution at the ready. The need to begin again, try another way, learn something and apply what is learned to another attempt is paramount here. Reward children who keep persevering to reach a solution.

Look for patterns

Rationale

Discovering the patterns in groups of numbers can be fun, apart from being very useful in solving problems. The discovery of patterns in number makes mathematical relationships more interesting and engaging for children. The ability to manipulate numbers using pattern formations leads to a strong understanding of mathematical thinking.

Teaching the strategy

Patterns may be in an arrangement of elements or in the form of a sequence. Both have rules which children must learn to recognise. The following points should be considered in teaching problem solving using pattern recognition as a strategy.

1. **Recognise a pattern**
   Children should be able to recognise what is, and what is not, a pattern by recognising common elements. Ask them to discuss and record different types of patterns and where they are found. Shapes, sizes, numbers, letters, positions and colours can all form the elements of patterns. There are examples of patterns all around us in visual contexts. You can also ask children to explore musical patterns of sound and rhythm.

2. **Describe a pattern**
   Accurate descriptors are essential. Children should:
   - use words to explain the pattern
   - write them down so others can understand (for example, 'Three diamonds are followed by two stars')
   - use position words and ordinal numbers to assist explanation.

3. **Complete a pattern**
   Encourage children to recognise the pattern, check it and continue it as required.

4. **Give a rule for a pattern**
   If possible, children should express the rule in numerical terms (for example, 'It goes up by 7' should be expressed as 'The number plus 7').

5. **Use the recognition of rules to solve problems**
   Children should learn to detect where a pattern has been formed in the information given. Encourage them to use this knowledge in order to solve the problem.

Links to

Hot air!
pages 28-29

Activity no.	Activity title	Page no.	Learning objectives as taken from the Primary Framework for Mathematics		Problem-solving strategies
1	At the office	12	Using and applying	Solve multi-step problems	Work backwards
			Handling data	Solve problems by collecting, selecting, processing, presenting and interpreting data	
2	Dr Shock	14	Using and applying	Choose and use appropriate calculation strategies	Logical reasoning
			Calculating	Calculate mentally with integers and decimals: U.t ±U.t	
3	Wipe-out	16	Using and applying	Choose and use appropriate calculation strategies at each stage, inc calculator use	Read, plan, work, check
			Knowing and using number facts	Use knowledge of place value and multiplication facts to 10 × 10 to derive related multiplication and division facts involving decimals (eg 0.8 × 7, 4.8 ÷ 6)	
4	High life	18	Using and applying	Identify and record the steps or calculations needed to solve a problem or puzzle	Trial and improvement
			Calculating	Use efficient written methods to add and subtract integers and decimals	
5	Mother bird	20	Using and applying	Suggest, plan and develop lines of enquiry	Logical reasoning Trial and improvement
6	I-scream lady	22	Using and applying	Suggest, plan and develop lines of enquiry	Make a list
			Handling data	Solve problems by collecting, selecting, processing, presenting and interpreting data, using ICT where appropriate	
7	Pirates	24	Using and applying	Collect, organise and represent information and review methods	Work backwards
			Calculating	Use a calculator to solve problems involving multi-step calculations	
8	Magic girl: nails	26	Using and applying	Represent and interpret sequences, patterns and relationships	Act it out Logical reasoning
			Measuring	Use standard metric units of measure with decimals to two places (eg 4.25cm)	
9	Hot air!	28	Using and applying	Represent and interpret sequences, patterns and relationships involving shape	Look for patterns
			Understanding shape	Extend knowledge of properties of triangles and quadrilaterals and use these to visualise and solve problems, explaining reasoning with diagrams	
10	Magic girl: classroom	30	Using and applying	Suggest and test hypotheses	Act it out

At the office

Setting the scene

This is a group or paired activity. Aldo and Carla work in an office block. From the clues presented, ask the children to work out on which floors of the office block Aldo and Carla work. Children will find that they will need to discuss this activity at each stage and that there will need to be a consensus before moving each character – you will see a lot of head scratching! Stress that each step has to be correct in order to find the answer; one wrong move will place either Aldo or Carla in the wrong office. (NB: Count the ground floor as 'floor 1'.)

Solving the problem

Working backwards from the very last clue will help to solve this problem. Spatially this may be challenging for some children, in which case it would be useful to use either counters or the names of the characters on the board to plot their progress.

Key questions

Representing: *How would you record each clue? Although you can move Aldo and Carla on the screen, what other strategies can you use to ensure you are taking the correct steps?*
Reasoning: *What is the starting point for this problem? What information is the most important in helping you solve it?* (Knowing the final movements that take Aldo and Carla down to the ground floor.)
Communicating: *On which floors are their offices located? How can you clearly demonstrate that your answer is correct?* (Ask children to come to the board to show each character's movements.)

Differentiation

Less confident: Children may need support with their spatial learning for this activity. In this case it is important that the group talk to each other and that they agree the characters' locations at each stage. Use either the interactive whiteboard or a pre-drawn tower with counters as support when moving the characters. Play the activity on a number of occasions until the children become familiar with the 'working backwards' strategy.
More confident: Ask the children to create their own 'story' to challenge friends. It is important to note that the challenge increases with the number of stages in each story. Encourage creativity by explaining why the characters have to go up and down (maybe to get to the photocopier or for a meeting).

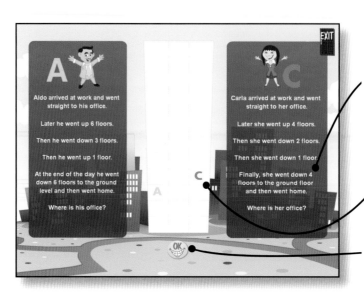

1. Follow each instruction carefully, starting with the final one. The clues change each time the activity is played.

2. Move the letters up and down to find the characters' offices.

3. Click 'OK' to check answers.

Name _____ Date _____

Aldo and Carla's new offices

📖 Aldo and Carla have changed offices. To which floors have they moved?

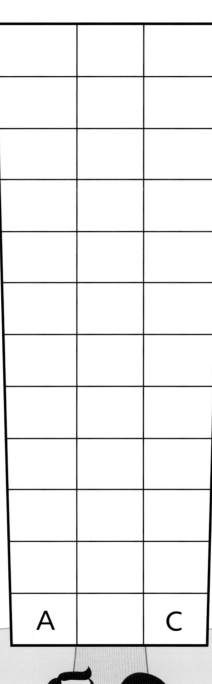

Aldo

📖 Aldo arrived at work and went straight to his desk.

📖 Later he went up 5 floors.

📖 Then he went down 3 floors.

📖 After that he went down 2 floors.

📖 At the end of the day he went down 5 floors to the ground floor.

Where is his office?

Carla

📖 Carla arrived at work and went straight to her desk.

📖 Later she went up 3 floors.

📖 Then she went down 10 floors.

📖 After that she went up 4 floors, then down 1 floor.

📖 At the end of the day she went down 4 floors to the ground floor.

Where is her office?

A   C

Dr Shock

- **Using and applying:** Choose and use appropriate calculation strategies
- **Calculating:** Calculate mentally with integers and decimals: U.t ± U.t

Problem-solving strategy

Logical reasoning

Setting the scene

This is a whole-class activity involving mental calculation with decimals. Explain that Dr Shock has a number problem based on a Carroll diagram; when the children solve the problems Dr Shock has a shocking surprise!

For the first problem, ask the children to look for any patterns to help find the missing total in the bottom right-hand corner of the grid. As the children progress through the activity, the number of blank squares with missing numbers increases, and the pattern changes. Children can click on the question mark beside the grid for a reminder of the original pattern.

Solving the problem

There will be a dictated path to follow but essentially the children should start by looking for two parts of a number sentence in order to fill in the missing pieces. As long as they understand that the ends of the rows or columns are essentially the solutions and that the green squares are the two parts of the sentence, they should be able to solve the problem by working round the square and filling in the blanks. It's much like a crossword - once you solve the obvious problems the answers to the others reveal themselves.

Key questions

Enquiring: *How will you find the missing numbers? How will you organise your thinking?*
Reasoning: *Which missing numbers should you find first?*
Communicating: *How were you able to find the total for the yellow square? How can you prove that your answers are correct? Can you prove that somebody has an incorrect answer?*

Differentiation

Less confident: Support children by writing out each part of the problem as a sentence. This will emphasise the mathematics behind each question and will give step-by-step guidance on how to approach the activity.
More confident: Ask the children to design their own 3 × 3 Carroll diagrams for a friend to complete. They should fill in the squares on one graph as an example, and give their partner another that is only partially filled in. Ask them what strategies they could use if information, such as a number within the four green squares, was missing. (Could addition sentences be inverted to subtraction sentences to find the smaller number?)

Follow up

Ask the children to complete the follow-up activity on page 15. Challenge them to find as many correct answers as possible for grids 3 and 4.

Problems bank

Page 35

Press the clue button for a reminder of the original pattern.

Fill in the missing numbers on the grid.

Name _____ Date _____

Shock treatment!

▨ Dr Shock has more problems that he wants to 'shock' you with.

▨ Can you solve these problems by filling in the blank squares? (Please note that in grids 3 and 4 there can be more than one solution.)

1.

2.3	3.7	
7.1	4.2	

2.

3.3	9.8	
8.1	4.2	

3.

		10.4
		5.2
7.2	8.4	

4.

		10.8
		10.4
7.8	13.4	

Wipe-out

Learning objectives

● **Using and applying:** Choose and use appropriate calculation strategies at each stage, including calculator use
● **Knowing and using number facts:** Use knowledge of place value and multiplication facts to 10 × 10 to derive related multiplication and division facts involving decimals (eg 0.8 ×7, 4.8 ÷ 6)

Problem-solving strategy

Read, plan, work, check

Setting the scene

This activity is suitable for groups or paired workers. The children must complete number sentences, using calculators as a tool. They can use their own calculators as well as the on-screen calculator when trying to work out problems. Before entering their answer into the on-screen calculator, the children must be sure it is correct; to do this they may need to test if it is possible to invert the numbers and still obtain a correct answer (see 'Solving the problem').

The first set of questions is based on converting numbers by addition and subtraction, and children are given three attempts at these. In the second set of questions children have to enter missing digits, demonstrating their understanding of place value, before entering the calculation on the calculator. Each correct answer wins a dolphin – when all the questions have been answered correctly, surf's up!

Solving the problem

Explain that each question gives two parts of a number sentence. Ask the children to tell you how they could use these parts to find the answer. Remind them about how inversions work (that is, that multiplications are inversions of divisional questions). Knowing this, are they able to use the numbers on the screen to find their answers?

Key questions

Representing: *How would you record the number sentences?*
Reasoning: *What mathematical sign would be appropriate for these questions? By inverting the question, are you able to prove that the sign you have used is correct?*
Communicating: *How can you prove that your answers are correct?*

Differentiation

Less confident: It is important that children understand that numbers do not change – it is just their place value that changes. In this case it maybe useful to change the place value to show something familiar. For example, 0.8 × 6 = 5.6, but what would be more familiar is 8 × 6 = 56. Also highlight that two parts of the question have been given and that the children are only looking for one part of the question.
More confident: Use a 'broken calculator' model; explain that the calculators the children are going to use do not have a working number 5. Encourage them to explain how they will answer their questions and prove that their answers are correct.

Follow up

Use the problems on page 17 to follow up this activity. Remind the children that they may use calculators. There is more than one possible solution for each problem.

Problems bank

Page 36

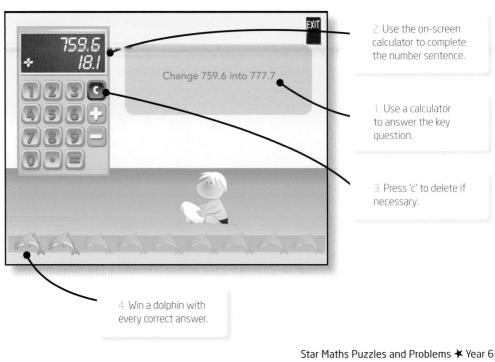

2. Use the on-screen calculator to complete the number sentence.

Change 759.6 into 777.7

1. Use a calculator to answer the key question.

3. Press 'c' to delete if necessary.

4. Win a dolphin with every correct answer.

Name _____   Date _____

Broken calculator

- Use your calculator to work out the next series of Wipe-out problems.

- Unfortunately, the number 5 on your calculator does not work and cannot be used.

- How will you solve these problems to prove you are correct? Show how you worked them out.

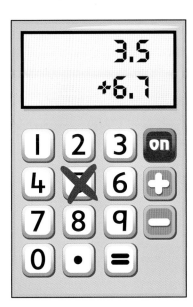

=
_____

Calculator display showing: 5.4 -4.1

=
_____

=
_____

=
_____

High life

Setting the scene

This is a whole-class activity. Greebly, Moylon and The Flut want to know who has the most money. Read the clues carefully, then click on the money and drag it to each character. Explain that each character has a different amount of money and that the clues will help the children to work out how much each should have.

Solving the problem

This type of problem relies on trialling and improving ideas until a final answer is reached. Remind the class to use the clues to support any working out. To begin the process, ask some of the children to have a guess at how much they think each character should have – this can be a useful starting point, but remind the children that they can change the order and amounts for each character at any stage.

Although the problem is most easily solved by trial and improvement, other strategies could also be useful. For example, looking for clues such as working out the difference between the largest and smallest amounts, or initially dividing the total amount by 3 and working backwards can also be helpful.

Key questions

Representing: *How will you begin to work this out? What resources could you use to help you?*
Enquiring: *How would you work out each step? What lines of enquiry will you follow?* (For example, trial and improvement strategies.)
Reasoning: *Why have you given the characters these amounts of money? How will you check that you have the correct answer?*
Communicating: *What is the answer to the problem? How did you arrive at the answer? Can you show this problem as a completed number sentence?*

Differentiation

Less confident: Use classroom money to support any strategies and to help the children to visualise the problem more clearly (though using some money images, found in most interactive whiteboard programs, could work as well).
More confident: Probe for alternative methods of solving the problem. Extend children by asking them to challenge a friend by creating their own problems in the same format. They should start by working out how much money each character has, then write clues for their friend to use to solve the problem. Remind them to state how much money there is and how much more or less the characters each have.

Learning objectives

● **Using and applying:** Identify and record the steps or calculations needed to solve a problem or puzzle
● **Calculating:** Use efficient written methods to add and subtract integers

Problem-solving strategy

Trial and improvement

Follow up

In the problem on page 19, Big Cheese, Greebly and Sparkles are trying to work out who is the richest. Encourage the children to work out how much each character has.

Problems bank

Page 37

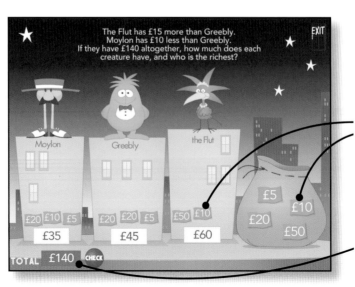

1. Drag and drop money from the bag to each of the characters.

2. A running total registers at the bottom of the screen.

Star Maths Puzzles and Problems ✦ Year 6

Name _____   Date _____

Loads of money!

- Greebly, Big Cheese and Sparkles are trying to work out who is the richest.
- Solve the problems below and then add the totals together to find out who has the most money!

1. Sparkles has £15 more than Big Cheese.
Big Cheese and the Greebly have the same amount.
If they have £75 altogether, how much does each creature have?

Greebly _____   **Big Cheese** _____   **Sparkles** _____

2. Greebly has £10 less than Big Cheese.
Big Cheese and Sparkles have the same amount.
If they have £80 altogether, how much does each creature have?

Greebly _____   **Big Cheese** _____   **Sparkles** _____

- Add up the totals. Who has the most money?

Greebly   Big Cheese   Sparkles

Mother Bird

● **Using and applying:** Suggest, plan and develop lines of enquiry

Problem-solving strategies

Logical reasoning
Trial and improvement

Setting the scene

This is a group activity. Mother Bird has to collect worms for her chick and take them back to the nest witihin a limited number of steps. The children have to determine what path she should take, using the arrow keys on the keyboard to direct the bird. The game is lost unless all the worms are picked up by the shortest route. If Mother Bird successfully brings all the worms back to the nest, the game automatically moves on to the next level. Each level is progressively more difficult as the worms begin to move!

Solving the problem

Although this is a 'logical reasoning' activity (finding ways to reach each worm via the shortest route so that the chick is reached most efficiently) it is, to begin with, solved with a degree of trial and improvement. Allow the children to try any strategies but encourage them to begin to look for patterns, emphasising that they are looking to find the shortest route.

Key questions

Representing: *How would you record the route? Could it be recorded as a set of instructions such as north five places, east six places, and so on?*
Reasoning: *What are the key stages that would ensure the most efficient route? Discuss what would be a bad route, and why.*
Communicating: *What is the most efficient route? How did you arrive at it?*

Differentiation

Less confident: Support the children as they try to find a suitable route for Mother Bird to take. Encourage the group to question each others' routes in order to begin to look for shorter distances for the bird to take.
More confident: The more attempts children have at this problem, the faster they will be able to plot the shortest route. Encourage them to think of some 'golden tips' that you could share with the whole class.

Follow up

Ask the children to use the grid on page 21 to find the shortest route to collect all the litter and bring it to the recycling bin.

Problems bank

Page 38

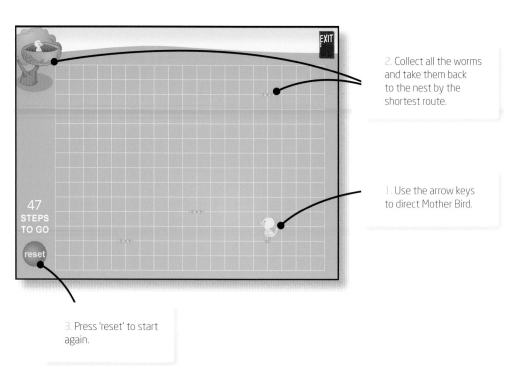

2. Collect all the worms and take them back to the nest by the shortest route.

1. Use the arrow keys to direct Mother Bird.

3. Press 'reset' to start again.

Name _____   Date _____

Collecting litter

- Guide your team around the playground to collect all of the litter.
- What is the shortest route? How many steps do you need to take?
- Can you collect all of the litter in under 52 steps?

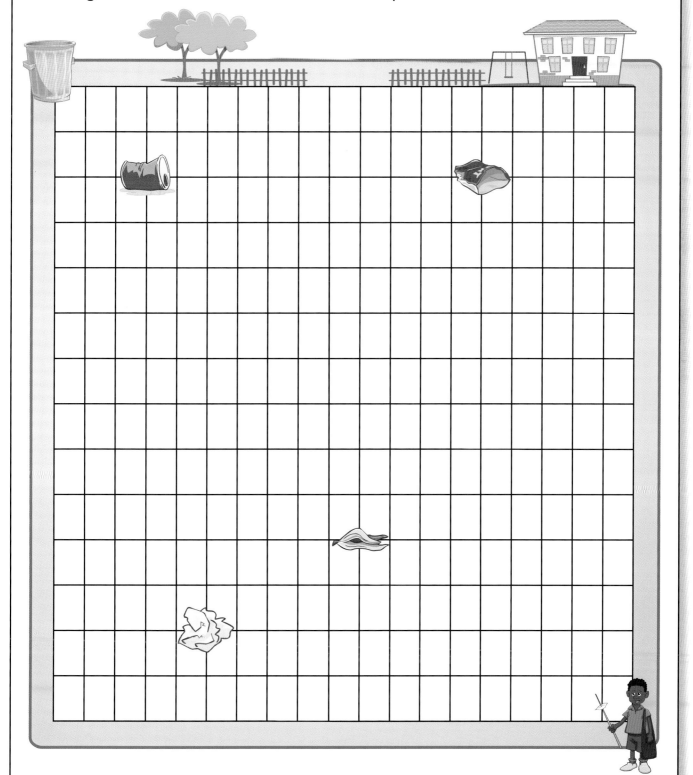

I-scream lady

● **Using and applying:** Suggest, plan and develop lines of enquiry
● **Handling data:** Solve problems by collecting, selecting, processing, presenting and interpreting data, using ICT where appropriate

Problem-solving strategy

Make a list

Setting the scene

This is a whole-class activity. The I-scream lady has set up a shop and wants to offer the greatest possible variety of combinations for her famous 'two-scoop ice creams'. The children have to work out the total number of possible combinations. They also have the option of adding either a wafer or a cherry topping, which increases to the number of possible combinations. Point out that some customers might buy a cone with two scoops of the same flavour ice cream.

Solving the problem

Writing a list is an efficient method and should help the children to organise their thinking. Start by creating a number of random combinations and ask if they can see any patterns. After a few combinations they should be able to see a pattern forming. Explain that although they could find each combination by randomly selecting flavours this would not support any predictions for the total number of combinations. Ask for suggestions about what line of enquiry they might take and draw out any reasonable ideas before asking the class to work out how many combinations there might be.

There are, in total, 27 possible combinations. Ask the children to show how they were able to find out the various combinations and what strategies they used. Identify the use of organised lists by demonstrating a pattern of answers such as:

Vanilla strawberry
Vanilla strawberry cherry
Vanilla strawberry wafer

Vanilla chocolate
Vanilla chocolate cherry
Vanilla chocolate wafer (and so on)

Key questions

Representing: *What would be the best way to record the variety of ice-cream combinations?* (Using a list or table.)
Enquiring: *What methods will you use to find the answer? How will you organise the data? Are you able to predict the number of combinations?*
Communicating: *How many combinations are there? How could you present your data to prove this is the correct answer?*

Follow up

The children should use a similar strategy to solve the 'Mr Smoothy' problem on page 23. However, in this activity the number of combinations will be less because for each smoothie two fruits will be blended to create one drink (for example, apple/nectarine is the same as nectarine/apple). Remind the children that one option is to have no topping on their smoothie selection.

Differentiation

Less confident: Use coloured cubes to represent the ice creams. Encourage the children to follow a pattern (as outlined above) as they make combinations from the cubes.
More confident: Extend the activity by explaining that the I-scream lady has decided to add chocolate buttons to the list of possible toppings. Ask: *How many combinations would there be now?*

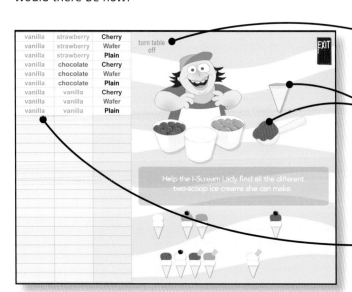

3. Choose to show or hide the table.

1. Drag the scoop and click on an ice-cream flavour to scoop it out, then place it on the cone to select the flavour.

2. The list builds up as each combination is selected.

Problems bank

Page 39

Name _____   Date _____

Mr Smoothy

- Mr Smoothy wants to know how many different combinations of smoothie he can make from the selection of fruits he has in his shop.

- Each smoothie is made from two different types of fruit with the option of a topping of Froze-Banana or Apple-Bites. How many combinations does he have altogether?

- The fruits are: strawberry, raspberry, apple and nectarine. The two additional options are a Froze-Banana or Apple-Bites.

Fruit	Fruit	Optional topping

Pirates

Setting the scene

This is a whole-class activity. Pirate Pete had found a treasure chest full of money, but has lost a lot of it in many different ways. We know how much he has now, but he doesn't know how much he has spent. The children will need to work backwards to help Pirate Pete calculate how much money he started with.

Solving the problem

Explain Pirate Pete's problem to the children, but ask them to discuss possible strategies for solving it in talk groups. Ask them to feed back ideas, with the aim of identifying key strategies such as breaking down parts of the problem (for example, working out how much he pays his crew in total). 'Chunking' parts of the costs together will make the overall problem more manageable.

This is a logic problem and needs to be worked out in stages. Although parts of the problem can be identified in isolation (such as the crew's costs), the actual differences need to be worked out step by step to find the total cost. Children also need to work systematically, starting with the amount of treasure that Pirate Pete had left and then working backwards.

Key questions

Representing: *How could you record how much money Pirate Pete has left after each stage and how much he started with?*
Enquiring: *What steps will you have to take in order to organise the information about Pirate Pete's treasure?*
Reasoning: *How can you use the information given to find how much money Pirate Pete started with? What could you use to keep track of the different stages involved in solving the problem?* (Perhaps organising the notes in a list or table.)
Communicating: *What is the answer to the problem? How did you arrive at it and how can you demonstrate that you are correct?* (Encourage the children to show the steps of the problem - perhaps using a calculator to demonstrate calculations.)

Differentiation

Less confident: Work with the children on one part of the puzzle at a time. Ask them to keep a running total of what Pirate Pete is spending. Provide a list or table to help them with this task.
More confident: The activity could be drawn up as a simple financial budget table with 'in' and 'out' payments. Challenge the children to set out the costs so that they are clear and easy to interpret.

1. Encourage the children to record the information provided in this box in a list or table.

2. Use these buttons to work backwards and forwards through the problem.

Name _____ Date _____

Captain Cranky

▥ Captain Cranky comes home each month with a ship full of booty! Unfortunately there are a number of sea things he must pay for. Help Cranky work out how much booty he has left over for the next two months.

Month 1

At the end of the month Captain Cranky gave each of his seven crew £150.

He gave his daughter, Sea Princess Scarlet, half the amount left.

He spent £120 on equipment.

He gave his favourite charity £700.

He is left with £900.

How much did Cranky start with? _____

Month 2

At the end of the month Captain Cranky gave each of his six crew £190.

He gave his son, Cabin Boy Chris, half the amount left.

He spent £700 on new rigging.

He gave his favourite charity £1000.

He is left with £4200.

How much did Cranky start with? _____

▥ How much did his children receive altogether? _____

Magic girl: nails

Setting the scene

This activity is aimed at groups or paired workers. Magic
girl will perform a hat trick if the children are able to solve
a puzzle from her bag at three levels.

The children start by choosing a ball from the bag, then
follow the directions to accurately mark out where Angelina should
place the nails in her DIY task. They then need to work out what the
total distance should be between the first and the last nail. They
have the option to change the point of view and to move the ruler and nails around
the screen until they feel confident that they are able to give a solid answer.

Solving the problem

The option of different perspectives can be useful when working with a group. It is
important to highlight that there may be more than one way to approach the problem
in order to get to the same answer. Emphasise the need for group members to
collaborate to solve the problem.

The problem can be solved in two ways. Either a child can physically set out the
nails (or a suitable resource) or they can extract the useful data from the question.
In the example shown below, the key data are 5 (for five nails) and 0.75 (the
measurement between each nail).

Key questions

Representing: *How would you record the measurements?*
Enquiring: *Do you need to place all the nails in order to answer the question? In
knowing the total distance between the first and last nail, how can this help in
keeping your intermediate nail measurements accurate?*
Communicating: *Are your marks or drawings accurate? Is another person able to
follow them? Do they help you to answer the question?*

Differentiation

Less confident: There are three levels in this activity with A being the least difficult.
Ensure the children start with level A before moving on to levels B and C.

If possible, invite the school caretaker into the classroom to give a practical
demonstration of the problem. Ask him or her to bring a short piece of wood and some
nails. The group can then follow the question and mark where the nails should be
pinned. Ask the caretaker to check for accuracy.

More confident: Extend the children by asking questions such as: *How many nails
would you use if you followed the instructions from 0cm to 10cm? Are you able to
finish the pattern at 10cm? Can you predict how many nails you would need for 20cm?*

1. Click on these buttons
to change the point of
view.

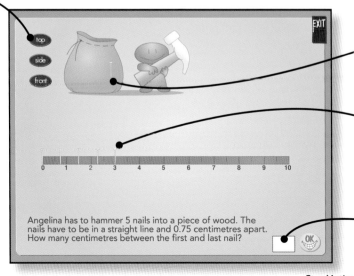

2. Drag the ruler onto
the page from the bag.
Then drag out as many
nails as you require.

3. The nails can be
dragged and positioned
at any point on the ruler.

4. Type the answer
into the box.

Angelina has to hammer 5 nails into a piece of wood. The
nails have to be in a straight line and 0.75 centimetres apart.
How many centimetres between the first and last nail?

Name _____ Date _____

More nails

◢ Angelina has to hammer in some more nails.

◢ Use a pencil to draw a small circle to mark on the rulers below where each nail should go.

1. Angelina has 7 nails. She hammers each nail 0.25 centimetres apart.

What is the distance between the first and last nail? _____ cm

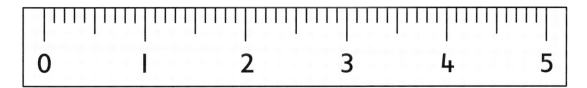

2. Angelina has 9 nails. She hammers each nail 0.2 centimetres apart.

What is the distance between the first and last nail? _____ cm

3. Angelina has 5 nails. She hammers each nail 0.4 centimetres apart.

What is the distance between the first and last nail? _____ cm

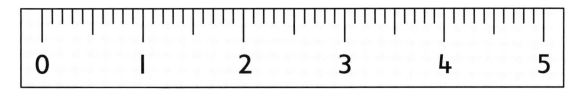

4. Angelina has 7 nails. She hammers each nail 0.5 centimetres apart.

What is the distance between the first and last nail? _____ cm

Hot air!

- **Using and applying:** Represent and interpret sequences, patterns and relationships involving shape
- **Understanding shape:** Extend knowledge of properties of triangles and quadrilaterals and use these to visualise and solve problems, explaining reasoning with diagrams

Problem-solving strategy

Look for patterns

Setting the scene

This activity can be played either as a whole class or as a group. Explain that Sebastian's hot-air balloon needs to get lighter and rise higher in order to break the world record. With each correct answer, he can drop a sand bag and rise higher. The problem relies on the children being able to predict and use patterns that involve both colour and shape. There are eight levels to this problem and at each level players are presented with a grid that has one missing piece. These grids become more challenging as the children progress through the problem. At each level they should identify what type and size of shape they are looking for, along with the appropriate colour.

Solving the problem

For each of these problems there are two elements to unpick:
1. What is the key shape/size in the pattern?
2. What is the key colour?

Explain that both are needed to complete the sequence accurately. Ask what sort of things children would need to discuss in order to accurately find the correct missing shape. Identify a confident group to lead a discussion about one of the more challenging sequences at the end of the lesson.

Key questions

Representing: *How would you show your results? What would be the best way to record your patterns so that you could discuss them later with the class?*
Enquiring: *What questions would you ask each other about the shapes and the types of pattern created? How could you begin to answer them?*
Communicating: *What is the answer to the problem? How would you explain that your shapes are correct? What patterns have you found? Do some have sequences that go beyond the missing piece?*

Differentiation

Less confident: Stress the importance of breaking down the problem (in this case, into colour and shape). Focus on one part at a time and ensure that each stage is clearly understood before combining them.
More confident: Encourage the children to make a note of the patterns they have found along with the missing shape so that they are able to explain any patterns to the rest of the class during the plenary.

Follow up

Ask the children to solve the problems on photocopiable page 29, involving Sebastian's friend, Barney the Balloonist.

Problems bank

Page 42

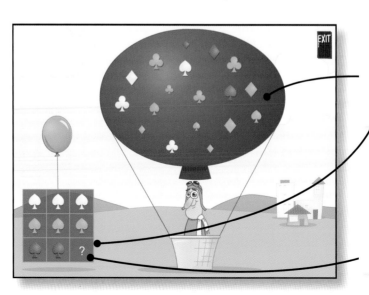

1. Drag and drop shapes from the balloon into the blank square in the grid.

2. If correct, the grid will automatically float up and show a new pattern. If incorrect, players will be asked to try again.

Name _____ Date _____

Rising high!

◢ Barney the Balloonist is trying for an altitude record. There are eight good flying weeks a year. In the first week he is able to fly up to 1200m and with each new attempt he is able to increase that distance by 125m. How high does he reach by week 8?

Week	1	2	3	4	5	6	7	8
Height	1200m							

◢ Barney also runs a very successful ballooning company. In April, when he starts, he makes £300 profit. For each consecutive month he doubles his profit from the last. How much money does he make in November?

Month	April	May	June	July	Aug	Sep	Oct	Nov
Profit	£300							

◢ Barney's company is so successful, he buys a new balloon that costs £7800. He bought the balloon on credit with interest payments of £56 added each month. If he wants to pay it off in 12 months, how much will his total monthly payment be?

_____

Magic girl: classroom

Learning objectives

● **Using and applying:** Suggest and test hypotheses

Problem-solving strategy

Act it out

Setting the scene

This activity is aimed at groups or paired workers. The group must solve a problem from Magic girl's bag of tricks, at three levels, to see her perform a hat trick.

The children choose a level from the bag by clicking on one of the three balls. They have to find out how many desks are in Jana's classroom, based on the information given about the position of Jana's desk in relation to the other desks in the room. Children can change the point of view and move the tables around the screen.

Solving the problem

The challenge is based on finding out where Jana's desk is, and working out from that the total number of desks in the classroom. Spatially this may be challenging for some children, in which case it would be useful to use counters to plot their progress.

The option of different points of view can be useful when working with a group. Highlight the fact that there could be many different ways of approaching the problem in order to get to the same answer. Stress the importance of group members listening to each other and collaborating to solve the problem.

Key questions

Representing: *How would you begin to answer this problem? What parts of the question are most important? Why?*

Enquiring: *What resources do you think you would need to be able to solve this problem? How would you begin to set them out?*

Reasoning: *What parts of the 'clue' would you try to solve first? How would you know that you have the correct answer?*

Communicating: *What is the answer to the problem? How did you find it and what does it look like?*

Differentiation

Less confident: Ensure the children start with level A, the least difficult level. Use classroom resources, such as building bricks or doll's house tables, to support them in visualising the activity. Alternatively, rearrange the classroom to mimic Jana's classroom for the whole class to physically act out the problem.

More confident: Ask the children to create their own problems for a partner with the same sort of format, but this time using 24, 25 or 30 desks. Remind them that, wherever they place Jana's desk, their instructions on where it is must lead their partner to be able to work out how many desks there are in total.

1. Click on these buttons to change the point of view.

Follow up

Introduce the problem on page 31. Jana is trying to organise a game in the playground. Can the children follow the instructions and organise her friends correctly?

Problems bank

Page 43

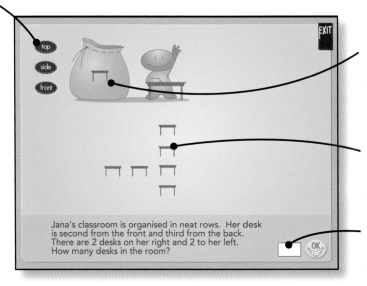

2. Drag and drop desks from the bag.

3. The desks can be moved around the screen and arranged in rows or columns.

4. Enter the answer in the box and click 'OK'.

Jana's classroom is organised in neat rows. Her desk is second from the front and third from the back. There are 2 desks on her right and 2 to her left. How many desks in the room?

Name _____   Date _____

Jana's games

🔖 Jana is trying to organise her friends to play two new games. Can you help her?

Game 1

Jana is organising her friends into rows. She is standing third from the front and fourth from the back. There are two children to the left of her and three to the right. Each row is full of children. How many children are playing her new game?

Game 2

Jana is second from the front, third from the back with three children to her left and one to the right. How many children are playing this game?

🔖 Work out the answers below. Draw a circle to represent each friend.

Game 1

Answer _____

Game 2

Answer _____

Problems bank overview

Fearless with fractions
Page 34

Problem-solving strategy: Work backwards

Knowledge of fractions comes into these equations. Children must understand that 1 whole is the 'whole job' or 'whole project' and that parts of it are complete, leaving a part not done.

Linked to activity: At the office

Using the equation
CD only

Problem-solving strategy: Work backwards

Introduce writing an equation in place of the diagram and the list. This is used when one result needs to be found using all the data. Introduce the term *inverse operation*. Discuss the meaning of *inverse* and show how the operation changes to its opposite when working backwards.

Vocabulary: *inverse operation*

Linked to activity: At the office

Some really big numbers
Page 35

Problem-solving strategy: Logical reasoning

Children have the opportunity to work freely and to discuss with a partner different methods of calculating and what answers make sense. Make sure they know how to check what constitutes a 'reasonable answer'. Remember, open-ended problem solving will take longer and much learning about strategies and good answers will take place with open-ended time as well.

Linked to activity: Dr Shock

On balance
CD only

Problem-solving strategy: Logical reasoning

The task is to determine 'If this is 1, then this is 2,' or similar. There may be more than one step in determining the value of a letter.

Linked to activity: Dr Shock

Arty Marty
Page 36

Problem-solving strategy: Read, plan, work, check

Allow extra paper for children to develop different solutions for this problem. Hold a class competition and work on this in spare time as well. Put completed solutions on the board for all to share.

Linked to activity: Wipe-out

Extreme sports
Page 37

Problem-solving strategy: Trial and improvement

Encourage the children to first read through the instructions carefully. Highlighting the main pieces of data is useful before starting to calculate. Point out which information is not useful to the solution.

Linked to activity: High life

Top Toys stocktake
CD only

Problem-solving strategy: Trial and improvement

Explain what a stocktake is. Children may have seen this happening in shops. Remind them to highlight only important information. Some information is not to be used (for example, *on a shelf, some more in a box, a heap in the corner* and *a few in a bag*).

Linked to activity: High life

For the tummy
Page 38

Problem-solving strategies: Logical reasoning / Trial and improvement

Including all possibilities for variety is a useful skill. Children need to see how a few items will increase the number of possibilites that have to be included.

Linked to activity: Mother bird

Problems bank overview

One move at a time
CD only

Problem-solving strategy: Logical reasoning

Perseverance is the main skill to use. Children must develop the skill of 'If at first you don't succeed try, try again'. Concentration and recording their moves are also important skills.

Linked to activity: Mother bird

Marketing madness
Page 39

Problem-solving strategy: Make a list

Encourage the children to carefully work through the information given and record it fully – they must not jump to conclusions. Remind them that full understanding of working mathematically involves careful notation of possibilities.

Linked to activity: I-scream lady

Shopping spree
Page 40

Problem-solving strategy: Work backwards

Firstly, the children must find the item that has the given price. Write it down, then list the other items in reverse order. Make the calculations according to the directions in the text.

Linked to activity: Pirates

Rates and charges
CD only

Problem-solving strategy: Work backwards

Discuss bills and how they are constructed. Using rates and charges for different parts of a bill, children are gaining experience of real-life situations. They learn to subtract the initial charge (for example, the day rate), then divide the remainder to find the pro rata charges.

Linked to activity: Pirates

Properties
Page 41

Problem-solving strategy: Logical reasoning

When children understand the concept of *properties*, they have a greater understanding of how groups of objects belong together and what decisions can be made about them. Discuss how we know something is an apple, a triangle, a horse. What are the properties of these objects? Do they remain constant?

Linked to activity: Magic girl: nails

Step by step
CD only

Problem-solving strategy: Logical reasoning

After reading the problem, the children must work through it step by step – recording, reading, recording, reading. Make sure that once a piece of data is processed, it is applied to other decisions too.

Linked to activity: Magic girl: nails

Numbers hiding
Page 42

Problem-solving strategy: Look for patterns

Some trial and improvement is required here. Initially, there will be a guess as to how the series progresses in order to find the numbers hiding. Children may need to use extra paper to write the answers to question 1.

In the input/output section, a study of the relationship between the input and output columns will show how the pattern is formed and therefore how it can be continued.

Linked to activity: Hot air!

Paying for credit
CD only

Problem-solving strategy: Look for patterns

Discussion can begin with how easy it is to accumulate credit with cards and with a mobile phone. Then discuss how we must pay all the money back and that charges change according to how long we are in debt. Each problem is phrased differently and requires different operations to arrive at solutions.

Linked to activity: Hot air!

Kitchen maths
Page 43

Problem-solving strategy: Act it out

Guessing is the first step. After guessing, children then adjust their answers. Take them through the 'adjusting' step so that they are confident in this.

Linked to activity: Magic girl: classroom

Name _____ Date _____

Fearless with fractions

Calculate what fraction remains, then give it a value.

1. (a) At the car wash fundraiser on Saturday, the Splash Team washed $\frac{1}{2}$ the total cars, the Clean Team washed $\frac{1}{4}$ of the total and the Sudz Team washed the last 10 cars.

How many cars did the Splash Team and the Clean Team each wash?_____

_____

(b) Draw a diagram illustrating the fractional parts and numbers of cars to check your solution.

2. (a) When the house had to be painted, the O'Carroll family invited their uncles to help out. Uncle Noel painted for $\frac{1}{3}$ the total number of hours needed for the whole job, Uncle Joe painted $\frac{1}{4}$ of the total hours and Old Uncle Freddie managed $\frac{1}{6}$ of the hours. There were 15 hours of work left for Uncle Ted to complete the job.

How many hours did each Uncle work? _____

_____

(b) Draw a diagram to show your solution.

3. In the Chompy Chocolate Drive at their school, Class 5J sold 20%, 5S sold 30%, 6K sold 25%, and 10% was sold by 6C. The rest were sold by 6M for £450.

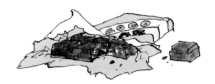

How much money did 5J and 5S each make? _____

_____

Name _____   Date _____

Some really big numbers

1. How many breaths do we take in a lifetime?

Working with a partner, count your breaths in one minute. Work out how many that is in a day, a year, a lifetime. Show your working and check it to be sure you have followed through with all the steps.

Is there a correct answer to this problem? _____

Explain. _____

_____

2. How many words can you read in a minute?

Working with a partner, read a page of a book which you can read fluently. Read for five minutes exactly. Mark the last word with your finger. Count the words read. Divide by 5.

Number of words I can read in a minute: _____

How many words would you read in an hour? _____

How many in 3 hours 15 minutes? _____

3. How many steps do you take in a day? You can wear a pedometer to count your steps or you can work out how many you think you take. Count the steps you take walking to various places around the school (such as the library, canteen, and so on). Estimate how many steps you will take getting home from school in the afternoon.

How many steps are you aiming to take today? _____

What will you have to do to make that many steps? _____

_____

Name _____　　Date _____

Arty Marty

1. In the rectangle below, draw lines from one side to another side to make 12 triangles. What is the least number of straight lines that you can draw to complete this challenge?

2. In this rectangle, draw lines from one side to another side to make 12 rectangles or squares. What is the least number of straight lines that you can draw to complete this challenge?

Name _____ Date _____

Extreme sports

▥ The Extreme Sports Competion will decide the champion mountain bike, surfing and diving contestant of the whole year.

1. In the Bike Bash on Wednesday morning, the points were close. Of the total points to be won, Bill Boulder scored 9s, 8s and some 7s and totalled 73. Jim Jet scored some 9s, 8s and 6s. His total was 77. Flailing Fred scored 9s, 7s and one 6, and totalled 77.

What were the three sets of scores? _____

_____

2. Our three fearless foes were rested and ready to go in the surfing competitions on Thursday morning. The total of the three scores was 225. Flailing is 10 points behind Jim and 20 points behind Bill Boulder.

What were their scores? _____

3. Friday was the diving competition and all were well trained. The dive scores were arrived at by judging style, form and precision. Bill Boulder's score was the sum of two primes between 30 and 40. Flailing Fred's score was the multiple of a prime number less than 20, and 5, while Jim Jet scored 15 less than a prime number between 80 and 90. The total of the three scores is 201.

What were their scores? _____

4. Who won the whole Extreme Sports Competition?

_____

Name _____ Date _____

For the tummy

1. At Pete's Place, there is a vast array of choices for pizza toppings. You may choose from Verry Veggie or Marvo Meat as a base, but you may order more cheese, tomato or seafood on top, or any two of these toppings as well.

Six friends walk into Pete's Place and think they will all have something different to each other so they can share.

(a) Will they be able to order all possibilities if they order one pizza each? _____

(b) How many choices are there? _____

Verry Veggie

Marvo Meat

2. Two families are going on a picnic. They decide to provide the food between them. The Gladstones will take the meat and bread and the Pedlars will take coleslaw, cucumber, tomato and lettuce. How many different sandwiches, with at least two fillings, can they make with these ingredients? _____

Sandwich

Name _____   Date _____

Marketing madness

1. The Bling Balloon Company wants to sell more balloons, so prize packs are made. On every third packet a bronze seal can be found, on every fourth packet a silver seal can be found, and on every fifth packet a gold seal appears. There is a major prize for the person who finds the packet with all three seals on it. How many would have to be made before this lucky packet appears?

Write the multiples down the list to see where they all meet.

Solution _____

3s	4s	5s

2. The Bling Balloons are sold in packs of ten and there are four different colours in a pack. There have to be three red balloons and two blue balloons in a pack, but there can be any number of yellows and purples. How many different combinations of the four colours can there be?

Make an organised list to show the different combinations.

Solution _____

Red	Blue	Yellow	Purple

3. At Dizzy Dan's Discount Store the Product Placement Department has a major problem with the placement of the latest range of Dizzy's Dishwashers. The Swisher, the Slosher, the Blitzer and the Ritzer are the models to be displayed in a line. The Slosher, however, cannot be placed next to the Ritzer, as it looks too inferior.

How many ways can the Placement Department arrange the dishwashers for display?

Solution _____

1st	2nd	3rd	4th

Name _____ Date _____

Shopping spree

🔹 Melissa, Anthony and Alexander are shopping. They love talking in riddles, however, so it is very hard to tell exactly what they spent.

1. Melissa bought a top, a skirt, a belt and some sandals. The top was £20 less than the sandals, while the skirt cost £6 more than that. The belt was a bargain at £20 less than the skirt.

If the sandals cost £49, how much did Melissa spend on each item and in total?

Top _____ Skirt _____ Belt _____ Sandals _____ Total _____

2. Anthony wanted to be outfitted correctly for the new football season. He went to buy boots, shorts, shirt and socks. His shorts were £10 less than the shirt, which was £20 less than the boots. His socks cost the least, a full £19 less than his shorts.

If his boots were £65, how much was each item and what was the total spent?

Shirt _____ Shorts _____ Socks _____ Boots _____ Total _____

3. Alexander went to the cash machine and drew out a large amount of money for his expenses. For Christmas presents for his family, he spent £15 more on books than on CDs, which cost £15 more than toys. Cards were one-fifth the cost of toys and one-third the cost of calendars, which were £36. Alexander now had £27 left.

How much did he get from the cash machine? _____

Name _____ Date _____

Properties

In these problems you must decide what the properties of the horizontal objects and the vertical objects are. From the given choices, decide on one which will fit both the horizontal and the vertical groups.

1.

a. The horizontals are _____

_____

b. The verticals are _____

_____

c. My choice is the _____

because _____

2.

	27	24	54
16			
28		72	44
56		32	80

a. The horizontals are _____

_____

b. The verticals are _____

_____

c. My choice is the _____

because _____

3.

	64	100	36
72			
120		256	42
56		96	48

a. The horizontals are _____

_____

b. The verticals are _____

_____

c. My choice is the _____

because _____

Extra challenge

4.

	49	81	144
6			
21		36	24
55		16	66

a. The horizontals are _____

_____

b. The verticals are _____

_____

c. My choice is the _____

because _____

Name _____   Date _____

Numbers hiding

1. What numbers are hidden under the squares marked with an X?

a.

1				X					28
	X	37							
								X	

b.

1				17					37
		X						X	
				X					

c.

									X
				X				32.5	
		X							16
14.5		X							1

2. Complete the magic squares.

a.

8	1	
3		
4		2

b.

11	7	3
		10

3. Write each rule. Then fill in the blank spaces.

a.

Input	Output
1	5
2	8
3	
	14
	17
7	

b.

Input	Output
1	1
2	5
3	9
4	13
	21
8	
	37

c.

Input	Output
1	2
4	17
6	37
7	
	65
15	
	401

_____   _____   _____

Name _____ Date _____

Kitchen maths

🔲 It's holiday time and Mrs Murphy is baking and cooking for her large family.

1. Mrs Murphy has four cups of flour in the pantry. The recipe for the cake needs $\frac{1}{4}$ cup more of flour than the pies and she will completely use up the four cups. How much flour is required for both recipes?

Guess	Check
Guess	Check
Guess	Check

Solution _____

2. When Mrs Murphy cuts three pies, she gives slices to her neighbours. She gives adults twice as much as children. If she gives pie to fewer than five adults and to the same number of children, what fraction of a pie will she give to each?

Guess	Check
Guess	Check
Guess	Check

Solution _____

3. To make a fruit salad Mrs Murphy needs a total of 25 pieces of fruit. She has twice as many kiwi fruit as peaches and the same number of apricots as bananas. There are more strawberries than any other fruit (six times the number of apricots). How many of each does she have?

Guess	Check
Guess	Check
Guess	Check

Solution _____

Teacher's name _____

Star Maths Puzzles and Problems diary page

Activity title	Children who used activity	How was activity used	Date used

Star Maths Puzzles and Problems ★ Year 6
PHOTOCOPIABLE

Activities answers

Aldo and Carla's new offices – page 13

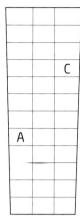

Shock treatment – page 15 (possible solutions given here for grids 3 and 4)

1.

2.3	3.7	6
7.1	4.2	11.3
9.4	7.9	17.3

2.

3.3	9.8	13.1
8.1	4.2	12.3
11.4	14	25.4

3.

6	4.4	10.4
1.2	4	5.2
7.2	8.4	15.6

4.

0.8	10	10.8
7	3.4	10.4
7.8	13.4	21.2

Broken calculator – page 17 (possible solutions)
1. 3.4 + 0.1 + 6.7 = 10.2
2. 4.4 – 4.1 + 1 = 1.3
3. 3.67 + 4.34 + 1.01 = 9.02
4. 4.74 – 3.11 + 0.01 = 1.64

Loads of money! – page 19
1. Greebly £20, Big Cheese £20, Sparkles £35
2. Greebly £20, Big Cheese £30, Sparkles £30
3. Sparkles

Collecting litter – page 21 (possible solution)

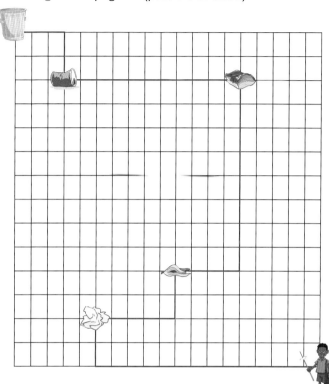

Mr Smoothy – page 23
1. 18 different options (don't forget one option is to have no topping!)

Captain Cranky – page 25
1. Month 1 = £4490
2. Month 2 = £12,940
3. Children = £7620

More nails – page 27
1. 1.5cm
2. 1.6cm
3. 1.6cm
4. 3.0cm

Rising high – page 29
1. 2075m
2. £38,400
3. £706

Jana's games – page 31
1. 6×6 = 36
2. 4×5 = 20

Problems bank answers

Fearless with fractions – page 34
1. **(a)** Splash Team 20; Clean Team 10
   (b) Teacher check
2. **(a)** ($\frac{3}{12}$ = 15 hours) Noel 20; Joe 15; Freddie 10
   (b) Teacher check
3. (15% = £450) 5J £600; 5S £900

Using the equation – CD only
1. 24; M + 4 – 6 = 22 so M = 22 – 4 + 6
2. 50; C – 20 + 52 – 13 = 69 so C = 69 + 20 – 52 + 13

Some really big numbers – page 35
Teacher to check answers for all three questions.

On balance – CD only
1. **(a)** AAAAAA
   (b) AAAAAAAAAA
   (c) AAAAAAAAAA
   (d) AAAAAAAAAAAAAAA
   (e) AAAAAAAAA
2. **(a)** GGGGGGG
   (b) GGGGGG
   (c) GGGGGGGGGGGGGG

Arty Marty – page 36
1. Teacher check
2. Teacher check

Top Toys stocktake – page 37
1. Blue 30, red 15, green 45
2. Shelf 40, box 65, corner 95
3. Baby Dollies 6, Sukie Sues 12, Cute Cathys 7

Extreme sports – CD only (one possible solution given here for question 1)
1. BB 3 × 9, 4 × 8, 2 × 7; JJ 3 × 9, 4 × 8, 3 × 6; FF 4 × 9, 5 × 7, 1 × 6
2. FF 65, JJ 75, BB 85
3. BB 68 (31 + 37), FF 65 (13 × 5), JJ 68 (83 – 15)
4. Bill Boulder

For the tummy – page 38
1. **(a)** no
   (b) 20 (don't forget to include the 2 plain options)
2. 10

One move at a time – CD only
1. **(a)** (RRB – B; R – BRB; – RBRB; BR – RB; BRBR – ; BRB – R; B – BRR; BB – RR)
   (b) 8
2. Teacher check

Marketing madness – page 39
1. 60
2. 4 combinations:

Red	Blue	Yellow	Purple
3	2	1	4
3	2	2	3
3	2	3	2
3	2	4	1

3. 12

Shopping spree – page 40
1. Top £29, skirt £35, belt £15, sandals £49. Total £128.
2. Shirt £45, shorts £35, socks £16, boots £65. Total £161.
3. £300. Books £90, CDs £75, cards £12, toys £60, calendars £36.

Rates and charges – CD only
1. **(a)** 185km
   (b) £212.35
2. 3
3. **(a)** 18 min
   (b) 14 min
   (c) 29 min

Properties – page 41
1. **(a)** regular quadrilaterals
   (b) irregular quadrilaterals
   (c) square
2. **(a)** divisible by 3
   (b) divisible by 4
   (c) 72
3. **(a)** square numbers
   (b) divisible by 8
   (c) 256
4. **(a)** square numbers
   (b) triangular numbers
   (c) 36

Problems bank answers

Step by step – CD only

1. Blue

	Blue	**Red**	**Green**	**Yellow**
Ben	✗	✗	✗	✔
Peter	✗	✗	✔	✗
Barry	✔	✗	✗	✗
Sunil	✗	✔	✗	✗

2. Goalie

Person	**Position**	**Award**
Simon	centre	M.I.
James	forward	B.G.
Daniel	goalie	B & F

3. (a) Joe
(b) Kamir

Person	**Food**	**Sport**
David	pies	soccer
Joe	chips	cricket
Kamir	fruit	rugby

Numbers hiding – page 42

1. (a) 13, 34, 82
(b) 49, 69, 97
(c) 46, 38.5, 26.5, 11.5

2. (a)

8	1	6
3	5	7
4	9	2

(b)

4	9	8
11	7	3
6	5	10

3. (a) 3 × input + 2; 11, 4, 5, 23
(b) 4 × input − 3; 6, 29, 10
(c) input^2 + 1; 50, 8, 226, 20

Paying for credit – CD only

1. £150, £200, £250, £300, £350, £450, £600
2. (a) £4700, £4600, £4400, £4000, £3200, £1600, nil, nil
(b) November
3. (a) £1405, £1310, £1215, £1120, £1025, £930, £740, £455; balance after 8 months is £740.
(b) £75
4. £692

Kitchen maths – page 43

1. $1\frac{7}{8}$ cups pies; $2\frac{1}{8}$ cups cakes
2. 4 adults $\frac{1}{2}$ pie each; 4 children $\frac{1}{4}$ pie each
3. 3 peaches, 6 kiwi fruit, 2 apricots, 12 strawberries, 2 bananas

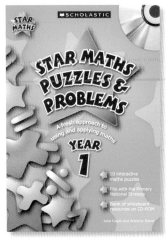

■SCHOLASTIC

Also available in this series:

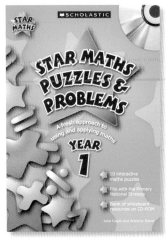

ISBN 978-1407-10031-9

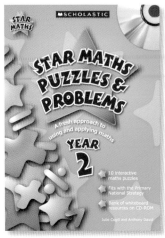

ISBN 978-1407-10032-6

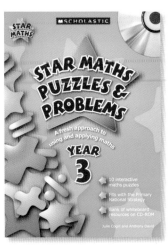

ISBN 978-1407-10033-3

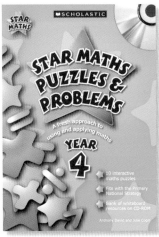

ISBN 978-1407-10034-0

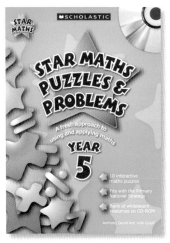

ISBN 978-1407-10035-7

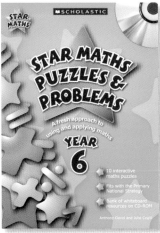

ISBN 978-1407-10036-4

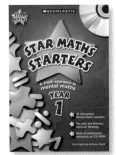

ISBN 978-1407-10007-4

ISBN 978-1407-10008-1

ISBN 978-1407-10009-8

ISBN 978-1407-10010-4

ISBN 978-1407-10011-1

ISBN 978-1407-10012-8

To find out more, call: 0845 603 9091
or visit our website www.scholastic.co.uk

The wait is over

The Duke and Duchess of Cambridge presented the prince to the world's media outside the Lindo wing at St Mary's Hospital just over 24 hours after he was born. The royal couple's happy news dominated headlines around the globe as the world joined in Great Britain's widespread celebrations

BUCKINGHAM PALACE

Her Royal Highness The Duchess of Cambridge was safely delivered of a son at 4.24 pm today.

Her Royal Highness and her child are both doing well.

Signed ....

....

....

....

 22ⁿᵈ July, 2013

CONTENTS

.Mirror DAILY

A Mirror publication
Head of Syndication & Licensing: Fergus McKenna
Mirrorpix: David Scripps
020 7293 3858

Produced by Trinity Mirror Media
PO BOX 48, Liverpool L69 3EB
ISBN 9781907324215

Managing Director: Ken Rogers
Senior Editor: Steve Hanrahan
Senior Art Editor: Rick Cooke
Editor: Paul Dove
Compiled by: Alan Jewell and Chris Brereton
Designers: Lee Ashun, Glen Hind, James Kenyon

Part of the Mirror Collection
© Published by Trinity Mirror 2013
Images: Mirrorpix, PA Photos
Printed by Precision Colour Printing

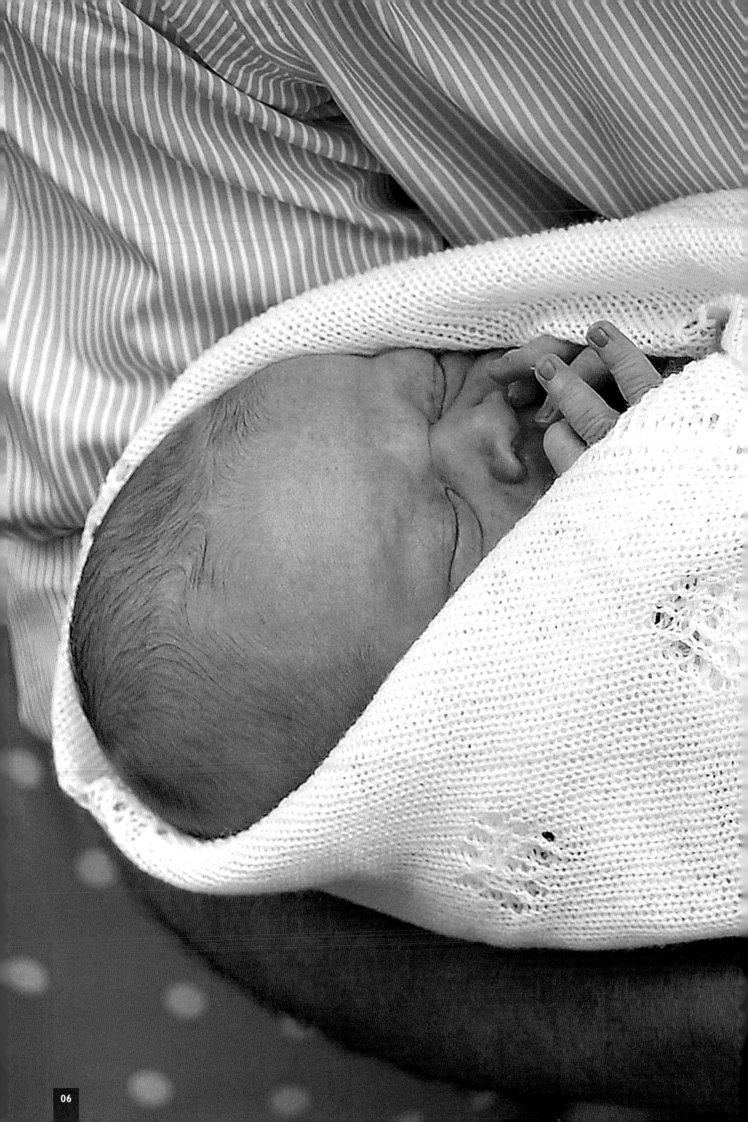

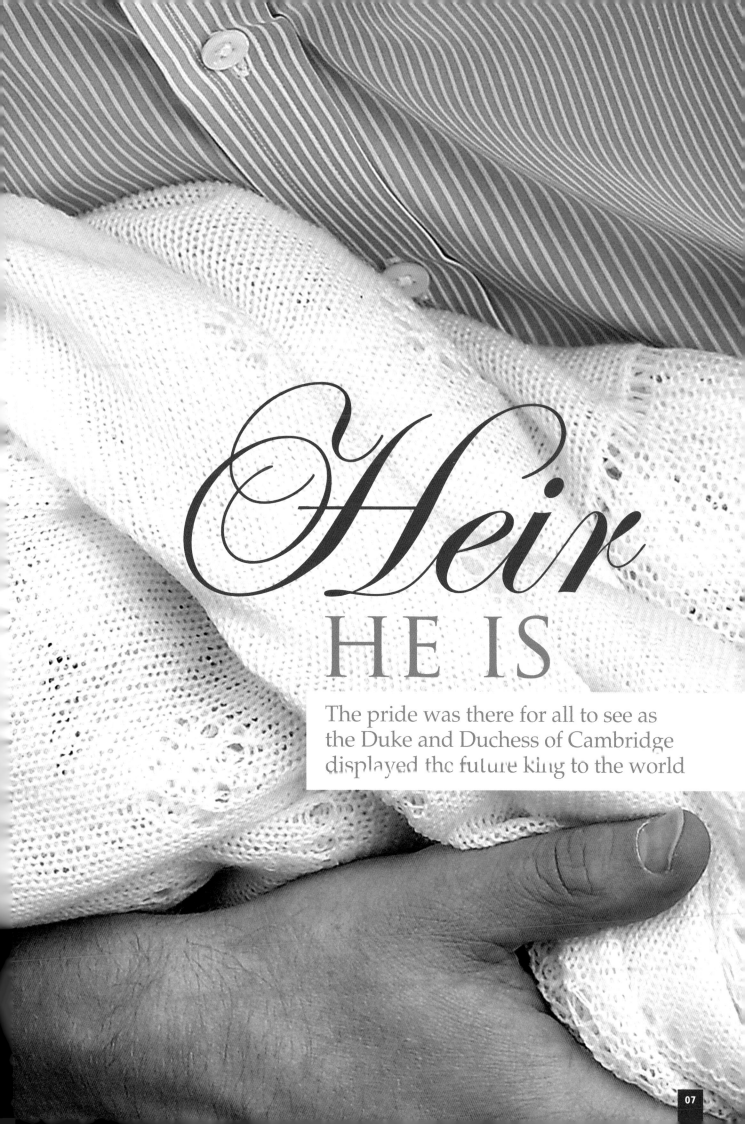

Heir
HE IS

The pride was there for all to see as
the Duke and Duchess of Cambridge
displayed the future king to the world

The Duke and Duchess of Cambridge present their son to the world's media

'He's a big boy, he's quite heavy. He's got a good pair of lungs on him, that's for sure'

– Prince William

It was the moment we got to meet our future king.

At 7.13pm on July 23 2013, the royal baby emerged with his proud parents from St Mary's Hospital in Paddington, London.

The most famous newborn child in the world made his first public appearance on the same spot where we were introduced to Prince William 31 years ago.

The Duke and Duchess of Cambridge posed for the massed ranks of photographers and television cameras with lenses focused on the tiny bundle wrapped in a white shawl that was initially cradled by Kate.

After a few moments the prince, whose delicate hands could be seen moving just above the shawl, was passed to his daddy and William and Kate moved forward to answer a few questions as cheers rang out from the patient well-wishers.

"He's got a good pair of lungs on him, that's for sure," William confirmed. "He's a big boy, he's quite heavy.

"We are still working on a name so we will have that as soon as we can. Wait and see. It's the first time we have seen him really so we are having a proper chance to catch up."

Kate, looking fabulous in a bespoke cornflower blue polka-dot Jenny Packham dress, was asked how she was feeling and admitted: "It's very emotional. It's such a special time. I think any parent will know what this feeling feels like." William concurred: "It's very special."

The Duke and Duchess disagreed over who their baby most looked like. "He's got her looks, thankfully," claimed William, but Kate interjected "no, I am not sure about that."

William was delighted to confirm that he had changed

The Duke of Cambridge looks ecstatic as he holds his newborn son outside St Mary's Hospital

Left:
The document announcing the prince's birth makes its way towards the easel at Buckingham Palace

Below:
The Changing of The Guard distracted the waiting crowd

his first nappy – "done that" – with an endorsement from Kate: "Yes, he was very good."

Asked about the baby's hair, William joked: "He's got way more than me, thank God."

With that, all three briefly went back inside, a Land Rover pulled up and William and Kate reemerged, this time with their son strapped into a car seat. Under intense pressure, William passed another test of parenthood as he secured the seat in the rear of the car at the first time of asking.

Kate sat alongside the baby in the rear of the vehicle as William drove his family to Kensington Palace for their first night together at home.

The photocall was the conclusion to a 36-hour period when the world's attention had been focused almost exclusively on the hospital.

It all started when Kate and William were driven to St Mary's from Kensington Palace at 6am on the 22nd with the Duchess in the early stages of labour. Official confirmation that a baby was on the way came an hour-and-a-half later.

She avoided the media representatives who were already in place outside by going in to the private Lindo wing through a back entrance, after protection officers carried out a security sweep of the immediate area.

While Kate had to do all the hard work, news reporters outside in the 32C heat had to fill time with waffle for the next 12 hours while events in the delivery suite remained a mystery.

Prince Charles was making an official visit to the National Railway Museum in York and was asked if he had any news about the birth. "Absolutely nothing at the moment – we're waiting," was the answer. As the labour continued, the Queen returned to Buckingham Palace having spent the weekend at Windsor and waited to hear from her grandson.

After a day of anticipation and seemingly endless speculation, the birth of a baby boy was finally confirmed at 8.29pm when Clarence House issued a formal press release via email and, moments later, posted the news on Twitter.

Shortly afterwards, at 8.48pm, there came a more traditional announcement, as the release was placed within a gilded wooden easel outside Buckingham Palace, where crowds had been gathering throughout the day in anticipation of the news.

The statement, on Buckingham Palace headed paper, was brought out for public inspection by Badar Azim, a footman with the Royal Household, and Ailsa Anderson, the Queen's press secretary. The easel, in the Rococo revival style, was previously used to announce the birth of William in 1982.

The news was also given out by Tony Appleton, a town

Kate Middleton's mother, Carole, and father, Michael, beam with delight after visiting their grandson

crier, on the steps of the Lindo wing. "May he be long-lived, happy and glorious, and one day reign over us," he announced.

The birth had occurred at 4.24pm but official confirmation was delayed to allow the new parents to spend precious time with their son and inform family members, such as the Queen, Prince Charles, Prince Harry and Kate's parents, Carole and Michael Middleton, in a flurry of phone calls.

The Queen is now the first living monarch to see a great-grandchild born in direct succession since Victoria 120 years ago. As a result, the monarchy has three generations of heirs to the throne for the first time since 1901.

The labour progressed normally and the man who delivered him, Dr Marcus Setchell, smiled broadly as he left the hospital that evening, remarking: "Wonderful baby... beautiful baby."

Hundreds of royalists, tourists and well-wishers joined media from all over the world in gathering outside St Mary's on the hottest day in Britain for seven years. When confirmation came, the celebrations started there and at Buckingham Palace, where people sang, danced and chanted in delight.

William spent the night at the hospital with his wife and child, a luxury not available to most fathers in the UK.

It was the first royal baby born in the Twitter age. By 8pm on the day of the birth, over 500,000 tweets were sent mentioning the baby, with a peak of 25,300 tweets per minute. Just 41% of those tweets came from the UK with 29% originating in the US.

The arrival of the new prince gave the nation another reason to celebrate during a summer of sporting success, which had seen a British man win Wimbledon, an Englishman claim the US Open golf championship, rugby union's Lions triumphant in Australia and England's cricketers win the first two Tests of the Ashes series.

To mark the birth, the London Eye was illuminated ➤

The country held its breath as the Duchess of Cambridge went into labour. Follow every moment from her admission to hospital to the birth of our future king

6 am

The Duke and Duchess of Cambridge arrive at St Mary's Hospital in Paddington, central London and are escorted into the exclusive Lindo wing, away from the eyes of the waiting media.

7.56 am

Kensington Palace finally confirms that Kate Middleton has gone into labour.
A statement read: "Her Royal Highness The Duchess of Cambridge has been admitted this morning to St Mary's Hospital, Paddington, London, in the early stages of labour.
"The Duchess travelled by car from Kensington Palace to the Lindo wing at St Mary's Hospital with The Duke of Cambridge."
A spokesman also confirms that the birth is going to plan.

9.02 am

Mervi Jokinen, of the Royal College of Midwives, tells reporters that Kate will have been delighted to go into labour, especially as it is the hottest day of the year.
She said: "It gets quite uncomfortable being pregnant in the heat. Your legs swell more. It's actually more uncomfortable. If you go into labour, it can be a relief."

10 am

KEEP CALM AND CARRY ON KATE

Twitter is flooded with good luck messages from around the world.
Broadcaster Piers Morgan tweets: "Keep Calm...and Carry On. Kate" and added: "My money's on an Australian cricket birth - all out by tea."
Labour's former deputy prime minister John Prescott jokes: "Great to hear the Duchess of Cambridge has gone into labour. Is she an affiliated member?"

Reporters wait for news

Town crier Tony Appleton outside the Lindo wing

10.45 am

Prime Minister David Cameron confirms again on BBC Radio 4's Woman's Hour that the child will one day be the British monarch, regardless of its sex.
"I can't claim any role in this one, I'm afraid, except one small thing - well, it's a big thing actually - which is to get all of the heads of the realms over which our Queen is Queen, to agree that whatever the sex of the baby that Will and Kate have, if it's a girl, it will be our Queen," he said.

11.28 am

Terry Hut, a 78-year-old from Cambridge who has camped outside the Lindo wing for 12 days in preparation for the birth, outlines his excitement.
"I have the best royal bed in town," he told reporters.
"At night we're watching the hospital in two-hour stints, like the Army.
"The health of the baby, and Kate, is the only important element."

11.36 am

An excited Prince Charles admits he is in the dark as to when the baby may arrive or what its sex is.
"I know absolutely nothing at the moment - we're waiting," he said when asked by a member of the public.

1pm

Well-wishers from across the globe begin to surround Buckingham Palace as they await news of the new birth. Grandmother Vivien Williams, who is visiting London with her family, told a group of reporters: "There are a lot of people here.
"It's quite a feature of British people to get into a frenzy about something."
The visitors' numbers swell even more when thousands clap and cheer the Changing The Guard, a ritual that is always popular during the summer months.

Obstetrician Guy Thorpe-Beeston, left, and Surgeon-Gyneacologists Marcus Setchell, centre, and Alan Farthing

Members of the midwife team cannot disguise their delight after their crucial role in delivering the royal baby

red, white and blue, while the BT Tower and Trafalgar Square were also lit up. The following day, the Changing of the Guard music at Buckingham Palace included 'Congratulations' 'Royal Salute' and 'The Duke of Cambridge March'. Elsewhere in the capital, the Honourable Artillery Company (HAC) fired a 62-gun salute from Tower Wharf at the Tower of London, while there was a 41-gun salute by the King's Troop Royal Horse Artillery in Green Park. At Westminster Abbey, where William and Kate married in 2011, the bells pealed in celebration for three hours.

Elsewhere in the commonwealth, Niagara Falls in Canada was given a blue hue, as were the parliament buildings in Ottawa and the CN Tower in Toronto. The New Zealand parliament in Wellington had a 21-gun salute and 37 landmark buildings were illuminated in blue.

After another long day of endless speculation, rumour and counter-rumour, the first visitors to see the baby were Kate's parents, who arrived at the hospital in a taxi at 3pm wearing beaming smiles, nearly 24 hours after he had been born. They spent just over an hour with their first grandson.

After emerging, Carole told waiting reporters the baby was "absolutely beautiful" and the new parents were doing "fabulously".

A little over an hour later, at 5.30pm, Prince Charles arrived with Camilla and both waved as they went inside for a 20-minute visit. It was an historic moment as three male heirs to the throne came together.

When Charles reemerged, he wore a broad smile as he described his grandson as "marvellous, thank you very much, absolutely marvellous – you wait and see, you'll see in a minute".

The wait was a bit longer – nearly an hour and a half, in fact – but it was well worth it to see the joy on the faces of the new parents as they cradled their preciousl son.

If the baby prince's genes and health prove to be as robust as the Queen's, he will be the monarch to take Britain into the 22nd century. Quite a thought but, of course, he has no idea of the future that is already mapped out for him. Whatever happens, it's going to be a lot of fun getting to know him over the years to come. ▪

2.26pm
The Duchess of Cambridge gives birth to a son weighing 8lbs 6oz. This news is not released at this time, as the speculation continues to grow.

Dame Helen Mirren, who famously won an Oscar for playing the Queen, hopes William and Kate have a little girl. "We need more Queens in our life", she said.

4.24pm
A Clarence House spokesperson finally confirms the fact that the Duchess of Cambridge has given birth. The news had expected to be announced on an easel in the grounds of Buckingham Palace but the royal family used the modern methods of email, Twitter and Facebook to tell the world.
Clarence House tweeted: "Her Royal Highness The Duchess of Cambridge was safely delivered of a son at 4.24pm.

8.24pm

8.48pm
The traditional easel – where Royal births have always previously been announced, is placed close to the gates of Buckingham Palace. The thousands in attendance scramble to take mobile phone pictures of the historic document.

Prince William is giving the job of placing the new-born prince in his car seat before the happy couple head home following the birth of their son

Giving
THE NATION
A PRINCE

From the moment the pregnancy was confirmed, the world watched and awaited the new arrival

THE announcement that William and Kate were expecting a baby was brought forward in dramatic fashion when the mum-to-be was admitted to hospital with severe morning sickness.

St James's Palace released a statement at 4pm on Monday, December 3 after the Duchess of Cambridge was suddenly struck down by hyperemesis gravidarum, a condition which only affects about one in 200 expectant mothers.

She was taken to King Edward VII Hospital in central London after being taken ill at her parents' home in Bucklebury, Berkshire, where the royal couple had spent the weekend. At the time she was approximately seven to eight weeks pregnant.

As it was so early on in the pregnancy, it is believed that only Kate's parents, Carole and Michael Middleton, had been told the good news before the illness struck.

Naturally enough, and because of the fraught nature of those early days, William and Kate had wanted to avoid a public announcement for at least a couple of weeks, possibly even until the 12-week scan had taken place.

Circumstances forced William into informing the Queen via a telephone call, while Prince Harry is said to have learned he was to be an uncle via email while serving in Afghanistan as an Apache pilot.

Consultant Daghni Rajasingam, a spokeswoman for the Royal College of Obstetricians and Gynaecologists, explained the nature of the Duchess's illness.

She said: "The diagnosis is given when women cannot keep food or fluid down because of severe vomiting. Those who are vomiting pretty much constantly and cannot keep any nutrients down need to be admitted to hospital."

The severity of Kate's condition was something of a shock as just three days previously she had looked bright and breezy while visiting her old primary school, St Andrew's in Pangbourne, Berkshire. She showed her sporty side by enthusiastically joining in hockey practice despite wearing three-inch heels.

Two days before that, William and Kate had spent the day in Cambridge, their first visit to the city since the Queen gave them their titles on their wedding day. ➤

The wedding day in April 2011. A baby has been eagerly anticipated ever since

Kate's hospitalisation with severe sickness had tragic consequences

Leaving hospital after the illness that prompted the pregnancy announcement

Saying hello to five-month-old James William Davies, who was named after her husband

An excited greeting for pupils at her old prep school in November 2012

Above:
Showing off her hockey skills just three days before she was admitted to hospital with severe morning sickness

Although there was a great deal of concern for the Duchess as she was treated in hospital, congratulation messages quickly flooded in from all over the world.

The Prime Minister, David Cameron, tweeted: "I'm delighted by the news that the Duke and Duchess of Cambridge are expecting a baby. They will make wonderful parents." There was also a statement from US President Barack Obama and First Lady Michelle, who met the royal couple shortly after their wedding. They said: "We extend our congratulations to the Duke and Duchess of Cambridge on the welcome news out of London that they are having a first child."

As Kate was unable to keep food down, she was hooked up to a drip and monitored closely as she experienced dehydration and fatigue. During her first full day in hospital William was by her side for over six hours.

Sadly, the royal baby story was to take a tragic turn after two Australian radio DJs duped the hospital treating Kate into releasing information about her condition with a 5.30am prank call. Pretending to be the Queen and Prince Charles, they conned a nurse into giving out personal details about the Duchess, which were broadcast

on Sydney station 2Day FM. There was fury when the hoax call was discovered, although the royal family did not comment officially as they said the incident was a matter for hospital staff.

Three days after the incident, Jacintha Saldanha, the nurse who took the original call and unsuspectingly put the DJs through to another nurse, was found dead in a suspected suicide. St James's Palace released a statement, saying: "The Duke and Duchess of Cambridge are deeply saddened to learn of the death of Jacintha Saldanha. They were looked after so wonderfully well by everybody at the King Edward VII Hospital, and their thoughts and prayers are with Jacintha's friends and colleagues."

The desperately sad news soured what should have been a joyous occasion as Kate recovered and was able to leave the hospital after staying for three nights.

Ten days after being discharged from hospital, Kate made her next public appearance at the BBC Sports Personality of the Year awards at the ExCeL Arena in London. She presented a lifetime achievement award to Lord Sebastian Coe and the main prize of the evening to (the soon-to-be Sir) Bradley Wiggins. ➤

Prize girl

Right:
Presenting Bradley Wiggins
with the BBC Sports
Personality of the Year award

Below:
Chatting to another style
icon, David Beckham

'Kate appeared to reveal the sex of her baby by saying 'Thank you, I will take that for my d...' before stopping herself'

After a quiet Christmas, the royal couple decided to get away from it all early in the new year with a week's holiday on the Caribbean island of Mustique. They were upset when they were photographed on a beach and images were printed in an Italian magazine with Kate's baby bump visible as she was wearing a bikini. It was the same magazine that caused so much anger when publishing topless images of the Duchess the previous September.

Her first official engagement since the pregnancy was announced came at Hope House in Clapham, a residential treatment centre run by charity Action on Addiction, which she supports as a patron. With the bump obvious in a fitted dress, she animatedly chatted to women who had battled alcohol and drug problems. She appeared unaffected by another controversy not of her making – barbed comments by author Hilary Mantel that Kate was a "shop-window mannequin" who appeared "machine-made". The visit was made alone as William was on RAF search and rescue duties.

After a break in the Swiss Alps with William, where keen skier Kate had to avoid the slopes, she caused a stir on returning to Britain to meet youngsters supported by Prince Charles' charity, The Prince's Trust, in Grimsby. During a walkabout, Kate, wearing a burgundy Hobbs coat over a Great Plains dress, was presented with a teddy bear by a local woman, Diana Burton, and appeared to reveal the sex of her baby by saying: "Thank you, I will take that for my d..." before stopping herself. Another woman, Sandra Cook, overheard the exchange and told Kate: "You were going to say daughter,

*Talking to artist Paul Emsley after
viewing his official portrait of Kate at
the National Portrait Gallery in January*

The bump begins to
show in late February

Enjoying an exciting finish to a race at the
Cheltenham festival, alongside William

Receiving a teddy bear
during a walkabout in Grimsby

A light moment as her heel gets stuck in a grate during the Irish Guards' St Patrick's Day parade

Another teddy for 'bump'

Left: Pinning a special London Underground badge to her jacket, highlighting the extra passenger she was carrying

weren't you?" The blushing, flustered Duchess denied it, saying: "No...we don't know." The gender of a royal heir has never been revealed in advance.

After a day out at the Cheltenham horse racing festival on Gold Cup day, she was back on official duty when joining her husband at the Irish Guards' St Patrick's Day parade in Aldershot. She handed out shamrocks to the 1st Battallion Irish Guards but was left giggling in embarrassment when her stiletto became stuck in a drain.

The royal couple showed their caring side when visiting the headquarters of Child Bereavement UK, where they met children who had lost parents. Wearing a black Topshop dress and cream coat by designers Goat, the Duchess told Great British Bake Off judge Mary Berry that she was "a big fan of your cookbooks and your cakes". The following day Kate visited Baker Street tube station for an event to mark the 150th anniversary of the London Underground. She beamed when given a 'Baby on Board' badge and pinned it to her coat. ➤

Right: Helping out at a scout camp on a wintry day in Lake Windermere. Kate is a volunteer in the Scout Association

A busy week was completed with a visit to the Great Tower Scout Camp in the Lake District. Kate, a volunteer with the Scout Association and a lover of outdoor activities, braved wintry conditions to take part in the training camp, lighting fires and making bread twists.

In early April the expectant parents visited Glasgow, with Kate wearing a £425 navy and grey tartan jacket by English brand Moloh. They saw the Emirates Arena, a Commonwealth Games venue in 2014, and a charity that helped young people with drug and mental health problems. They were given a warm welcome, although four-year-old Shona Ritchie recoiled when William attempted to kiss her!

The bump was becoming more obvious when Kate attended a Scouts' Association awards ceremony at Windsor Castle. Wearing a Mulberry coat, she mingled with 400 scouts and was praised for being an "incredible role model" by chief scout Bear Grylls.

On St George's Day she visited a primary school in Wythenshawe, Manchester, wearing a tight-fitting floral dress as she planted a tree in the school grounds. She was presented with a book written by the pupils called 'What do Princesses Do?' As she read through the book, she recognised the description: "Eat bananas? Yes, I certainly do that. Dancing? Yes, that too. Eat sweets? Yes, I like all those!"

William and Kate were joined by Prince Harry for a fun day at the Warner Bros Studios in Leavesden, Hertfordshire. All three royals enjoyed a tour of the Harry Potter film set and gleefully brandished wands under the guidance of an instructor. They also saw props and costumes from the Batman film The Dark Knight Rises, and William was only too happy to climb aboard the Batmobile, the Tumbler. Kate looked stunning in a £38 Top Shop dress that sold out online within an hour of her being pictured in the polka-dot design.

William and Kate were apart on their second wedding ➤

Viewing a portrait of her husband and brother-in-law at the National Portrait Gallery

Left:
Attempting to weave some Harry Potter magic at the Warner Bros studios in Hertfordshire, alongside William and Harry

Below:
The centre of attention at a Buckingham Palace garden party, hosted by the Queen, on May 22

anniversary – April 29 – as the Duke was on search and rescue duty with the RAF in Anglesey. Kate spent the day visiting a children's hospice in Hampshire where the growing bump was visible in a coral Tara Jarmon coat and short peach dress. She politely declined the offer to join a group of children splashing around in a hydrotherapy pool.

Kate was wearing her favourite Top Shop polka-dot dress again in May as she and William attended the wedding of their friends William van Cutsem and Rosie Ruck Keene in Ewelme, Oxon.

The Duchess shone again at the Queen's Buckingham Palace garden party on May 22 where she dazzled 8,000 special guests in the season's hottest colour, a canary Emilia Wickstead coat topped by a white Jane Corbett headpiece, which she had worn at events in 2012.

Guest Susan Bradley, a Marie Curie nurse, said: "She recognised my uniform and told me our staff cared for her grandfather when he was terminally ill."

On June 4, less than six weeks before the baby was due, ➤

Below and right:
Looking up to a woman on stilts during a visit to a children's hospice in Winchester, Hampshire

William and Kate returned to Westminster Abbey, the scene of their wedding, to attend a service of celebration to mark the 60th anniversary of the Queen's coronation. Kate was wearing a bespoke peach Jenny Packham dress with a Jane Taylor hat. However, this was a rare occasion when she wasn't the centre of attention as it was very much the Queen's day.

On her last solo engagement before the birth, the Duchess officially named a new cruise ship in Southampton. The 1,000ft, 3,600-passenger liner 'Royal Princess' was inaugurated as Kate announced "May God bless her and all who sail in her", before smashing a large bottle of champagne over the hull. ➤

BumpWatch
How Kate's tummy grew during her pregnancy

January 11

February 19

March 5

March 17

Returning to Westminster Abbey, the venue for their wedding, to attend a service of celebration to mark the 60th anniversary of the Queen's coronation

March 19

March 20

April 4

April 21

Officially naming the 'Royal Princess' liner in Southampton

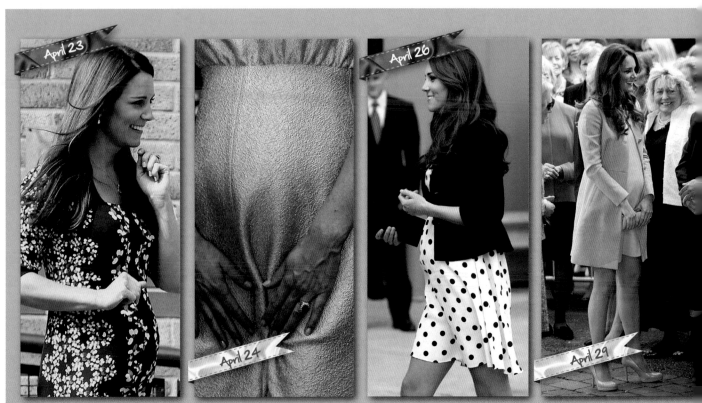

April 23

April 24

April 26

April 29

Looking to the skies during the Trooping the Colour ceremony

After attending the Trooping the Colour ceremony on June 15, and with a month to go before her due date, the Duchess disappeared from public view, missing the wedding of her friends Thomas van Straubenzee and Lady Melissa Percy the following weekend, although William did go.

In June it was confirmed that Kate would give birth at St Mary's NHS Hospital in London, in the same private Lindo wing where her husband had been born 31 years earlier.

The wing, which costs £4,965 for a 24-hour 'normal delivery', offers a luxury service similar to a high-end hotel. It was also confirmed that the baby would be delivered by Marcus Setchell, previously the Queen's gynaecologist, with assistance from Alan Farthing, the former fiance of murdered TV presenter Jill Dando.

Media pens were in place outside the hospital from July 1 as reporters and photographers from around the world prepared for the birth. Meanwhile, William took leave from his job to be at his wife's side while they waited for the baby to make an appearance. On July 8 it was announced that there would be another addition to the royal family as Zara Phillips and her husband, Mike Tindall, were expecting their first child early in 2014.

Then, after Britain had baked in two weeks of scorching weather, royal vehicles were finally spotted outside a back entrance to St Mary's at 6am on Monday, July 22. An hour and a half later, an official statement confirmed that the Duchess was in the early stages of labour, having travelled by car to the hospital with William from Kensington Palace.

It was the first stage of the news Britain had been eagerly anticipating. ■

May 22

June 4

June 13

June 15

WHAT KIND OF *Mum* WILL *Kate* MAKE?

At one stage she wanted to become a teacher and appears a natural with children, so Kate seems a perfect fit as a mum. But how difficult will it be to deal with the demands of parenting a royal baby?

IN almost 10 years of being known to the public since she began her relationship with Prince William, Kate Middleton has not put a foot wrong and it can be safely assumed that she is well capable of dealing with motherhood.

Although she came from a comfortable background and attended the exclusive Marlborough College in Wiltshire, Kate is, in royal parlance, a 'commoner', who met her handsome prince at university, fell in love and married him in a fairytale occasion watched all around the world.

She has established a connection with the British people because she has always exuded a confidence that has never hinted at arrogance. The eldest of three children, she has captivated through her elegant sense of style, charm and near ever-present smile.

An active, sporty woman, she has taken on royal engagements with ease and is said to be well-liked by the Queen for the positive way she represents the family.

Any controversies surrounding the Duchess of Cambridge have not been of her own making and have engendered sympathy at the heartless actions of others. In September 2012 she had to endure the publication of topless photographs taken while she and William were on a private

holiday in France, followed by the hoax call from two Australian DJs pretending to be the Queen and Prince Charles while Kate was in hospital, which culminated in the tragic death of a nurse who passed on the call.

Kate's pragmatic nature was seen in how the pregnancy was planned, waiting until after the Queen's Jubilee celebrations and a highly-successful Far East tour when she was taking anti-malarial tablets, which are a no-no during pregnancy.

Days before the pregnancy was announced late last year, Kate visited her old primary school, St Andrew's Prep in Pangbourne, Berkshire, and told pupils that she loved her time there so much that, at one stage, she wanted to return as a teacher.

At 31 and with a good deal of life experience already behind her, she is ready for the most important role an adult can take on.

Both her and William are keen to demonstrate a modern attitude to parenting. They met at St Andrews University and will want their child (and any future siblings) to follow a similar path, allowing them to meet and mix with people from different backgrounds.

Kate is said to be in contact with Mary, Crown Princess of Denmark, another commoner, in this case Australian-born, who married into royalty. Mary is a mother of four children and is believed

Clockwise:

Meeting a six-year-old cancer patient during a visit to Canada, July 2011

Chatting to a young girl, during the royal couple's first overseas tour

Meeting Raffaela Cheater, aged two, in Quebec

A big hug for Nancy Williams, three, during a visit to Alder Hey Hospital in Liverpool, February 2012

Happily posing for photographs at Alder Hey

to have offered Kate advice on how to juggle a royal role with family life.

It is likely that a nanny will not have such a significant role as in previous generations of royals. Some children were effectively brought up by hired help but Kate is keen to spend as much time with her baby as she possibly can.

It is believed that the royal couple don't intend to employ a full-time nanny and want to be as hands-on as possible. The intention is to use one on a part-time basis when they have to attend events and babysitters, such as Kate's parents, are unavailable.

However, the reality is there will be a demanding schedule of official engagements, ceremonies and overseas tours to undertake so it will be a tricky balancing act for the Duchess. Compromises will have to be made, probably by all sides, although formal foreign trips are off the agenda until next year. When Prince William was born in June 1982, his parents did not carry out a major tour for 10 months and when

they did – in Australia and New Zealand – William went with them.

As they adjust to parenthood, Kate and William will soon be living in a huge, 21-room refurbished apartment at Kensington Palace, having relished their largely peaceful, undisturbed existence at a farmhouse in Anglesey, where William has been based with the RAF. They rejected the opportunity to have servants and the Duchess said no to the offer of a dresser.

At their Welsh sanctuary, they did their own cooking and washing, while Kate was regularly spotted doing the food shop at the local supermarket. Such simple pleasures will be denied them from now on. The size of Kensington Palace means a staff is essential. Their life is even less their own.

Kate will also have to protect the baby from undue attention as it grows up. As a direct heir to the throne, interest in the royal child will be huge and there will be plenty of hazards to navigate as her and William

continued on page 38 ➤

Common touch

Clockwise:

Playing with a patient at Alder Hey

A friendly chat with three girls before the Diamond Jubilee Pageant on the River Thames, June 2012

Taking part in outdoor activities in Kent, June 2012

The Duchess was a hit on the royal couple's tour of south-east Asia, as the Mirror reported (above), with local children excited to meet her

Having fun with children from a primary school in the Solomon Islands, September 2012

Writing a birthday message for a leukaemia sufferer in Malaysia during a tour of south-east Asia

Kate seems able to establish an instant connection with children, as this delighted boy demonstrates during a visit to Newcastle, October 2012

'Kate has appeared to revel in her royal duties, most particularly the ones where she has got to mix with the public – children especially'

Kids are always happy to step forward and present Kate with flowers

raise the new prince in their image, and prepare him for his own future role.

The Queen is now into the seventh decade of her reign and Charles continues to wait for his turn, but over the past three years William and Kate have effectively become the figureheads for the royal family. It was they who revelled in the London Olympics, attending as many events as possible and clearly demonstrating how much they were enjoying themselves. Their refreshing attitude has endeared them to royal-watchers the world over.

When in April 2011 she stepped out onto the balcony of Buckingham Palace alongside her new husband, Kate's life changed forever. That evening, when they drove through London in an open-top Aston Martin with the 'JU5T WED' numberplate, they showed off their sense of humour and made clear they would not be suffocated by formality.

In the time since, Kate has appeared to revel in her royal duties, most particularly the ones where she has got to mix with the public – children especially. Now comes the big test of looking after her own, while remaining the most photographed woman in the world. It's a challenge she seems well set to master. ▪

Child's play

Top: *Meeting a baby in Grimsby during a visit to the town, March 2013*

Middle: *Spending time with three children while visiting the headquarters of Child Bereavement UK in Buckinghamshire, March 2013*

Left: *Admiring a girl's dress in Ipswich, March 2012*

William
APPLE *of*
DIANA'S EYE

He was born to be king but how will William fare as a father? With his caring, compassionate nature inherited from his mother, all the indications are that he should relish the role

*A*LL royal children have to cope with intense scrutiny but none have experienced a fiercer glare than the Duke of Cambridge – still 'Wills' to many – who grew up in an age of mass media and, as a 15-year-old, had to deal with his mother's tragic, and very public death.

It is to his credit that he remains as resolutely normal as it's possible for a royal to be. He married a 'commoner', his sweetheart from university, and they set up home in a cottage in Anglesey, where he was based as an RAF search and rescue pilot.

However, the royal couple have recently moved to Kensington Palace, Diana's former residence, as William prepares to take on greater responsibilities. With the Queen in her 88th year, more duties will fall on the Duke.

William admits that his mother had a profound influence on him and spoke of how much he missed her on his wedding day.

In an interview with American television in 2012, he said: "I prepared myself mentally. I didn't want any wobbly lips or anything.

"It's the one time since she died where I've thought to myself 'it would be fantastic if she was here', and just how sad really for her, more than anything, not being able to see it. ➤

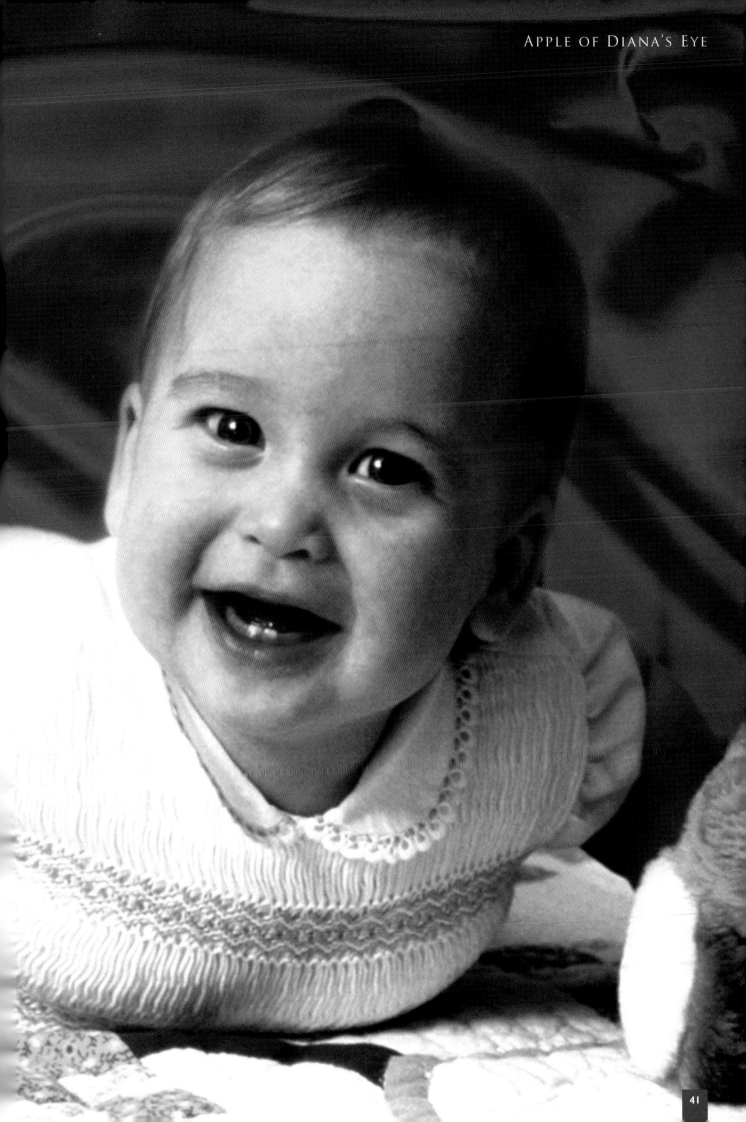

"I think she would have loved the day and I think, hopefully, she'd be very proud of us both. I'm just very sad that she's never going to get a chance to meet Kate."

It's inevitable that those same feelings will resurface as William adjusts to being a father and considers what it would have been like to share the experience with Diana – and what it would have meant to her to be a grandmother.

Alongside her eldest son's wedding, it surely would have been her proudest moment and her absence will be sorely felt. However, the approachable, open nature, combined with a sense of fun and adventure, which characterised her and is so evident in William, will surely be passed on to his children.

In the same interview, in May last year, William also described the difficulties he faces balancing his RAF career with increasing royal duties. Tellingly, he suggested a tipping point would arrive when he became a father.

He said: "It's a really difficult one because I really enjoy my time in the Air Force and I'd love to continue it. But the pressures of my other life are building.

"More importantly, I'd rather like to have children. So that's the key thing really."

continued on page 46 ➤

Diana, Charles and William, leaving hospital, June 1982

William gets in some practice for the future as he holds a three-week-old baby in London, April 2012

William's christening at
Buckingham Palace, August 1982

WILLIAM, 21.06.1982

There was a special sense of excitement surrounding the arrival of William, given his status as heir to the throne.

Princess Diana, who was still driving her Ford Escort the day before the birth, believed she was going to give birth on her 21st birthday – July 1 – but in the event her first child came 10 days earlier.

He weighed 7lb 1½oz when born at 9.03pm on a rainy evening after a 16-hour labour. When the news was announced, cheers erupted among those waiting expectantly outside St Mary's Hospital in Paddington. Before long, Prince Charles emerged to greet those outside and share his joy with the crowd, who joyously chanted "it's a boy" and "we want more".

In Buckingham Palace, the Queen was delighted when she was told that the baby had been born safely. She visited her new grandchild the following morning. Prince Andrew heard about the birth while serving with the Falklands task force, while Princess Anne was visiting the USA.

Mother and child left hospital 21 hours after he was delivered. Prince William was officially named seven days later, his full title being William Arthur Philip Louis.

The last King William was William IV, who was succeeded by Queen Victoria in 1837. Arthur was one of Prince Charles's own names, Philip came from the Duke of Edinburgh while Louis was a nod to the much-missed Earl Mountbatten, killed by an IRA bomb three years earlier.

William was christened two months later as a new royal era began.

IN THE NEWS
Celebrations continued after Britain liberated the Falkland Islands from the Argentinian Junta

England had qualified for the second stage of the World Cup in Spain after winning their opening matches against France and Czechoslovakia

ON THE BOX
Triangle
Wogan

TOP OF THE CHARTS
Goody Two Shoes, Adam Ant

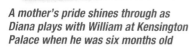

A mother's pride shines through as Diana plays with William at Kensington Palace when he was six months old

From boy to man

Clockwise:
Two images of Diana and William
when he was aged nine months,
March 1983

Showing affection to a young boy in
Sydney, Australia, January 2010

Talking to young children during a
visit to Glasgow, April 2013

Growing up fast, on tour in New Zealand, April 1983

Appearing to wave at the cameras, Aberdeen airport, October 1983

Now aged 18 months, December 1983

In the near future, he is expected to move from his current role and take up a position with the Household Cavalry, based either at the regiment's Windsor or Knightsbridge barracks. Remaining in the Armed Forces, amid speculation that he would have to give up his military career, should stave off full-time royal duties for now.

A source close to the Duke has said: "At present, William knows that he has a limited number of years before he must take on greater royal duties and there will come a time when he can no longer be an active serviceman, but he feels that time has not arrived yet."

He is very fond of the Middleton family and their closeness has always appealed to him, given it was something he didn't really experience as a boy. He will want the same for his child and we can also expect him to willingly embrace the nitty-gritty of changing nappies and taking his turn when the baby is awake at night.

It can only be hoped that the new royal baby enjoys a childhood free from the traumas that William experienced. Although he was showered with love and affection by Diana, with whom he had a special relationship, the horrific nature of her death in a Paris car accident in 1997 when he was just 15 must have caused unimaginable grief.

William demonstrated maturity and extraordinary composure far beyond his years on the day of her funeral, at a time when his mind was surely in turmoil.

Even before her death, he had to cope with his parents' failing marriage – they separated when he was 10 – and the very public recriminations that followed as accusations and arguments were played out in public.

Throughout all this turbulence, and as he progressed

In celebration of the birth of Prince George Alexander Louis of Cambridge, July 22, 2013

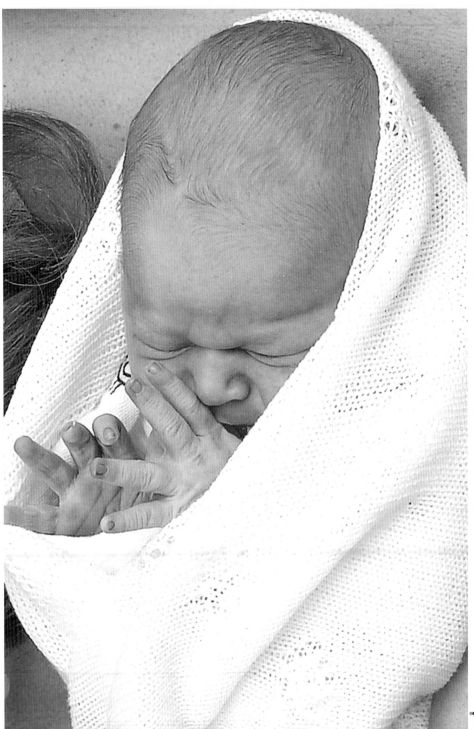

In celebration of the birth of Prince George Alexander Louis of Cambridge, July 22, 2013

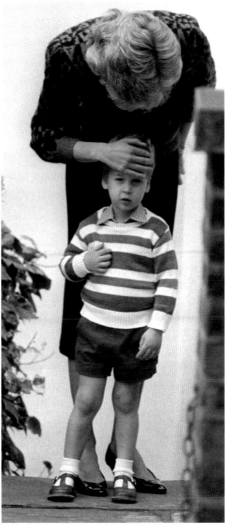

THE SADDEST DAY

Prince William was just 15 years old when he lost his mother in horrendous circumstances.

He was a relatively carefree teenager when he went to bed at Balmoral Castle on the evening of Saturday, August 30, 1997, but was awoken by Prince Charles the following morning to be told that Diana had died overnight in a Paris car accident.

The most important person in William's life was gone, while deep anger ensued over the way she was treated by the press and royal family.

Amid the firestorm, William had to, somehow, come to terms with what had happened.

On the Thursday, alongside his father and brother Harry, then 12, he stopped outside the gates of Balmoral to look at the flowers and messages left by the public. The following day, after returning to London, they did the same at Kensington Palace.

A day later, William said goodbye at her funeral, accompanying his father, brother, paternal grandfather and maternal uncle in walking behind the funeral cortège from Buckingham Palace to Westminster Abbey.

Growing up

Clockwise:
At a photocall to mark his second birthday, June 1984

First day at nursery, September 1985

A holiday in Majorca, August 1987

Watching a polo match, May 1987

Plenty of enthusiasm in Cambridge for William and Kate, increasingly the public face of the royal family, November 2012

Talking to a six-year-old boy in Canada, July 2011

from adolescence to adulthood, William maintained a quiet dignity, avoided any significant controversy and grew into a mature but modern figurehead for the royal family.

If she were alive today, Diana would have celebrated her 52nd birthday on July 1. She was days short of turning 21 when she gave birth to William and from then on he became her world – she described him years later as her "soul mate".

She adored William and the feeling was reciprocated. He honoured Diana by presenting Kate with her engagement ring, explaining "this was my way of keeping her close to it all". Also, the opening hymn of their wedding two years ago was Guide Me Oh Thou Great Redeemer, which closed Diana's funeral.

As she brought up William and Harry, Diana did all she could to break free of the rigid formalities and protocol of royalty to give them as normal an upbringing as possible. While they dutifully attended ceremonial functions, she also took them to theme parks. Although the boys grew up surrounded by wealth and opulence, she took them to homeless shelters so they could experience another side of life and appreciate that others are not so fortunate.

The influence she had covered nature and nurture. Tall, fair and bashful in a charming way, he demonstrates instinctive ease when meeting the public.

The fact that he appears ready to step away from his RAF career shows the importance William is placing on being present for his new family, on hand to experience all the fun of being a father in the years to come. ■

'From adolescence to adulthood, William maintained a quiet dignity, and grew into a mature but modern figurehead for the royal family'

Delivering a speech at a gala charity dinner at St James's Palace, October 2012

Showing Dad one of the Sea King helicopters he captains at RAF Valley, Anglesey, July 2012

Saying hello to a young baby in Cambridge, November 2012

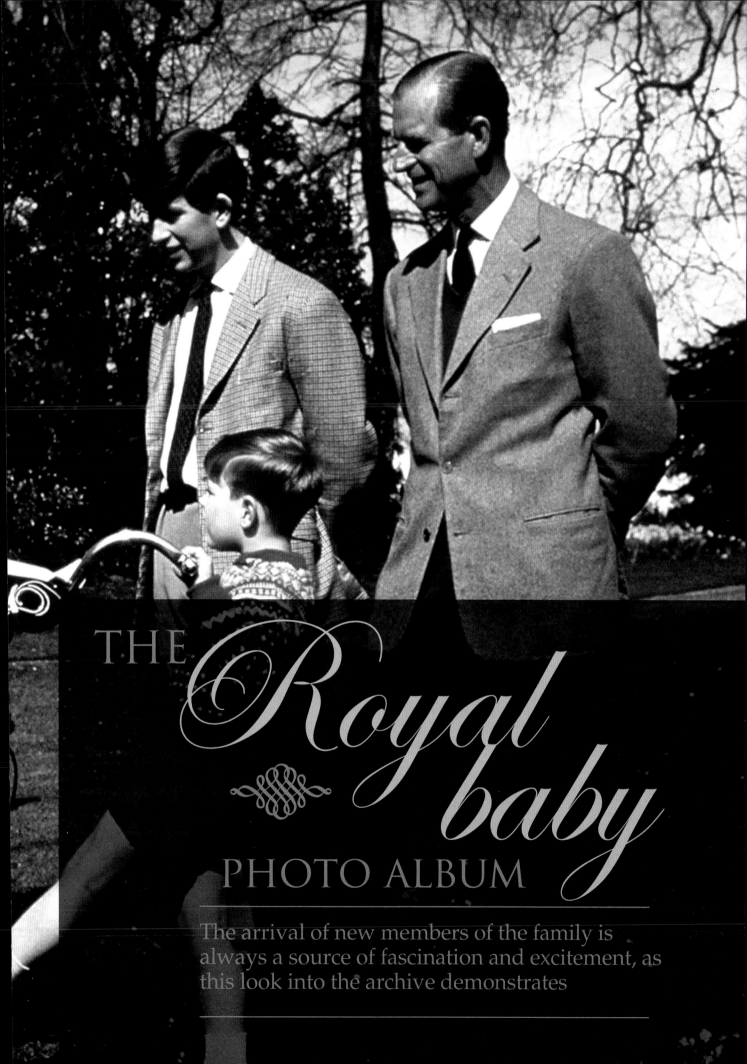

THE *Royal baby*

PHOTO ALBUM

The arrival of new members of the family is always a source of fascination and excitement, as this look into the archive demonstrates

The future King Edward VIII and King George VI in their prams, 1895

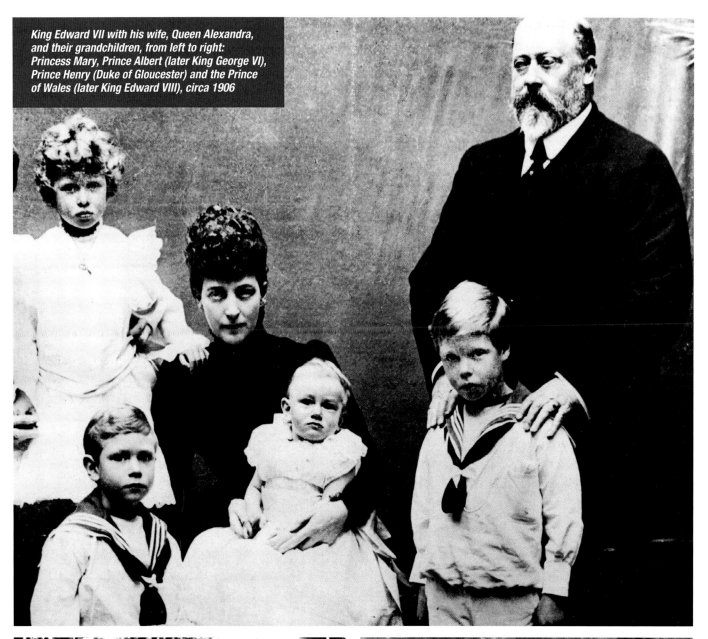

King Edward VII with his wife, Queen Alexandra, and their grandchildren, from left to right: Princess Mary, Prince Albert (later King George VI), Prince Henry (Duke of Gloucester) and the Prince of Wales (later King Edward VIII), circa 1906

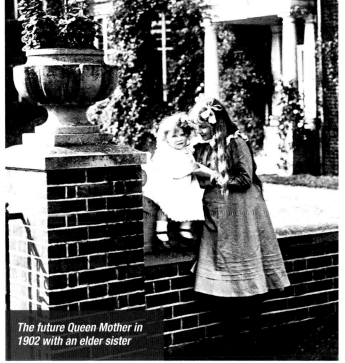

The future Queen Mother in 1902 with an elder sister

King George V and Queen Alexandra pose with their daughter, Princess Mary, and baby, July 1923

ELIZABETH, 21.04.1926

The woman who, as of July 2013, is the second-longest reigning monarch in British history was born at 2.40am at No. 17 Bruton Street, Mayfair, the London town house of the Earl and Countess of Strathmore, the parents of the then Duchess of York (later to become the beloved Queen Mother).

At 10am a statement confirmed that both mother and daughter were making "satisfactory progress" following the birth. It also said that "a certain line of treatment was successfully adopted", which was a cryptic method for avoiding saying that Elizabeth had been delivered by cesarean section.

Curiously, the following day's Daily Mirror reported that 'in accordance with custom the Home Secretary (Sir William Joynson-Hicks) was summoned to be at hand at the birth'.

It was a time of turmoil in Britain with Joynson-Hicks dragged away from talks to try and resolve a coal dispute, which would culminate in the commencement of the General Strike in May when for six days industries and services ground to a halt and workers took to the streets.

The royal birth was a source of joy and escapism for the public, as well as the immediate family. People lined the street outside Bruton Street, waiting to glimpse visitors. King George V and Queen Mary travelled by car from Windsor to see their daughter-in-law. The Prince of Wales, the Duke of York's older brother, telegraphed congratulations from Biarritz.

Exactly a month after the birth, the first picture of the new princess was released and her name was revealed: Elizabeth Alexandra Mary. Elizabeth after her mother, Alexandra after the late Queen Mother and Mary after the then Queen.

The Daily Mirror of April 22 had suggested she may be named Elizabeth. She was christened on May 29 in the private chapel at Buckingham Palace. Water brought from the River Jordan was used.

IN THE NEWS:
Prime Minister Stanley Baldwin was due to meet mineowners as the coal dispute continued

The then Duke and Duchess of York with the days-old Princess Elizabeth, April 1926

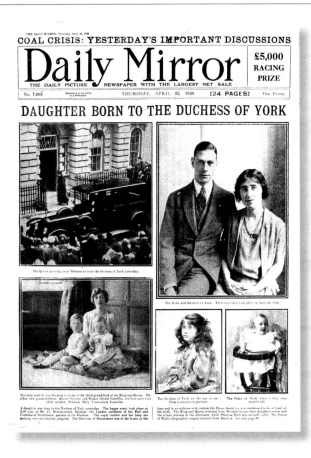

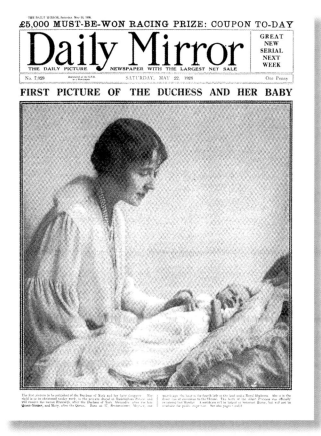

Daily Mirror front pages celebrating Elizabeth's arrival

A private photograph of baby Elizabeth and her parents, taken by a young holidaying couple whose car had broken down outside the royal couple's Scottish cottage and knocked on the door for help. The Duke and Duchess were happy to assist, providing water for the tourists to fill up their leaking radiator

Prince Philip, Elizabeth's future husband, aged 12 months in 1922

Elizabeth, nearly one, and her nanny, April 1927

CHARLES, 15.11.1948

The birth of Princess Elizabeth's first child was already well anticipated before his arrival on Sunday, November 14, 1948.

From early dawn on the 14th, hundreds of people gathered outside Buckingham Palace, watching and waiting.

Before going into labour, Elizabeth, described as 'radiant and cheerful' by the Daily Mirror, lunched with her husband, Prince Philip, and the King and Queen. Lobster, tongue and ham salad was on the menu.

When her son arrived at 9.14pm on the 14th, he weighed 7lb 6oz and was said to have fair hair like his father. He was delivered at Buckingham Palace.

At 9am on the 15th, the king's piper, Alec MacDonald, played a stirring Scottish tune on the bagpipes in the gardens of the Palace. Elizabeth smiled at the sound as, the Daily Mirror reported: 'It is her dearest wish that her son should share her love of Scotland and its traditions.'

The Mirror's celebratory editorial said: 'The aspect of the happy event which is likely to have struck people most forcibly is its highly modern character. This was shown in the ease and normality of the birth, and in the pre-natal behaviour of the mother. Clearly we have a royal family who have no sympathy with old-fashioned ideas in regard to the important matter of maternity.'

Like his mother, the baby boy's name was revealed a month after the birth on December 14, the eve of his christening. It was to be Charles Philip Arthur George, chosen for "personal and private reasons".

It was the first time in two centuries that Britain had a Prince Charles.

IN THE NEWS:
The British film industry was having to cut costs with film stars and producers asked to take a voluntary 25% cut in salaries

The Labour government said Britain was on the verge of a steel age, as it prepared to nationalise the industry

AT THE CINEMA:
Bonnie Prince Charlie (!)

A proud mum with her first child at his christening, Buckingham Palace, December 1948

A family portrait with King George VI on the left

Aged five months

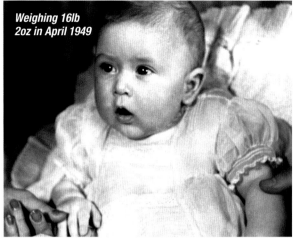

Weighing 16lb 2oz in April 1949

Lifted up by Dad in the grounds of Windlesham Moor, Surrey, July 1949

Playing in the cot outside on a summer's day

ICONIC SOUVENIRS

84-page glossy magazine specials

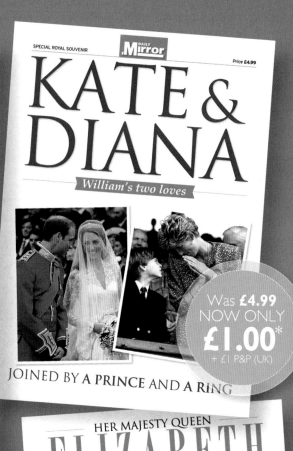
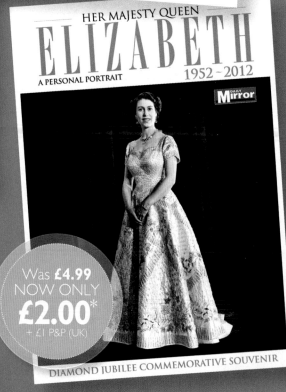

Above:
Anne's christening at
Buckingham Palace, with
Queen Mary pottering
about in the background,
October 1950

Right:
A portrait in the private
sitting room of Clarence
House, January 1951

Below:
The Daily Mirror carries
the first picture of
Princess Anne as she
receives a kiss from
her brother,
September 1950

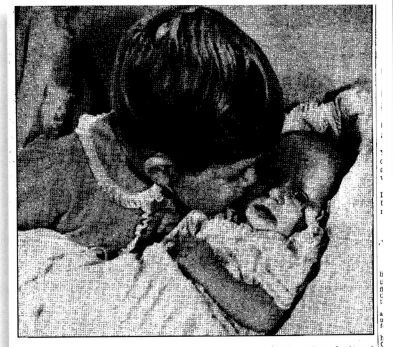

Princess Anne—the first picture

The first pictures of Princess Anne, daughter of Princess Elizabeth and the Duke of Edinburgh, are released this morning. They were taken by Cecil Beaton. Here are the little Princess and her brother Prince Charles, who will be two years old in November. —Another picture, back page.

The day they were born

ANNE, 15.08.1950

Less than two years after the birth of Charles, Princess Elizabeth was delighted to have a daughter, who was safely delivered at Clarence House.

Weighing 6lb, a girl had been the preference for Elizabeth and Prince Philip, according to the Daily Mirror's report the following day.

A dispatch rider left Clarence House just after the birth and went straight to the Home Office with news of the birth. From there, the story was flashed all round the world.

Waiting crowds learned of the birth when a secretary, accompanied by Prince Philip's personal detective, placed a sheet of paper inside an oak-framed notice board, which read: '15th August 1950. HRH Princess Elizabeth was safely delivered of a Princess at 11.50am today. HRH and her daughter are both doing well.'

The crowds surged forward and when the news was digested, cheers sounded for the new princess. Inside, a beaming Prince Philip handed glasses of champagne to staff.

The Daily Mirror's editorial read: 'Amid the stresses and anxieties that have come to make up the world's daily news, the people of Britain and the Commonwealth will be glad to turn their eyes to this family occasion for congratulation and rejoicing.'

The girl's name was revealed when she was two weeks old: Anne Elizabeth Alice Louise. It was reported that the first name had been chosen before the birth. For the previous three years, Anne/Ann had been the most popular girl's name, according to the announcements of births in The Times.

Obviously, Elizabeth was the Christian name of her mother and grandmother, Alice the name of Prince Philip's mother and Louise the feminine form of Louis – Earl (Louis) Mountbatten, then Chief of the Defence Staff – was Philip's uncle.

Anne made her first public appearance on the evening of September 17, heading for Balmoral with her mother on the 6.55 sleeper from King's Cross Station. Her christening was on October 21.

IN THE NEWS:
The Korean war raged between American and British troops and communist forces

ANDREW, 19.02.1960

Princess Elizabeth had become Queen Elizabeth II by the time she gave birth to her third child, nearly 10 years after Anne.

Prompted by the frequent comings and goings of royal doctors, a crowd of nearly 1,000 people waited outside Buckingham Palace on the evening of February 18 1960, anticipating the new arrival. Shortly after 10pm two officials of the royal household emerged to shouts of "What is it – a boy or a girl?" However, there was a sense of anti-climax when they told those gathered that the birth was not imminent.

It was at 3.30pm the following day when a boy eventually arrived, the news confirmed to those outside 45 minutes later by Palace superintendent Stanley Williams who placed a bulletin on the Palace railings. A loud triumphant cry of "it's a boy" broke out. He weighed 7lb 3oz. Bells rang in celebration all over the country.

Appropriately, given the baby's future career, the Admiralty sent an order to all ships and naval bases: 'Splice the mainbrace'. This meant that rum would be issued to toast the birth.

A 4ft-high stork made of hundreds of white flowers arrived at the Palace in a Jaguar. There was no indication who sent the present.

His name, Andrew Albert Christian Edward, was revealed on March 22, together with the first pictures of the new prince.

Andrew and Albert were the names of his grandfathers; Christian came from his great-great-great grandfather – King Christian the IV of Denmark – and Edward from his great-great grandfather – King Edward VII.

Christened on April 8, he was the first Prince Andrew for 500 years.

IN THE NEWS:
It was revealed that Prime Minister Harold Macmillan would decide whether to allow House of Commons debates to be televised

ON THE BOX:
Emergency Ward 10
Take Your Pick

TOP OF THE CHARTS:
Why, Anthony Newley

A proud grandmother on her 60th birthday, holding baby Andrew as Charles and Anne watch on

A stunning family image with Balmoral Castle in the background, September 1960

The Queen pushes Andrew around the grounds of Balmoral

The day they were born

EDWARD, 10.03.1964

The Queen's fourth and final child was a son who arrived a week early.

He came into the world at 8.20pm on Tuesday, March 10 at Buckingham Palace, weighing 5lb 7oz.

Immediately after the birth Prince Philip telephoned the news to the Queen Mother at Clarence House, Princess Margaret at Kensington Palace, Prince Charles at Gordonstoun School and Princess Anne at Benenden School.

The Queen gave birth in the Belgian Suite at the Palace. Her five-man medical team was headed by Sir John Peel, the gynaecologist who was present at the births of all her children.

ITV interrupted the opening of The Plane Makers at 9.13pm to announce the birth in a news flash. The BBC waited another two minutes for a scheduled bulletin.

Royal Navy ships fired their guns in salute and 12 RAF Lightnings flew over London, while flowers arrived at the Palace 'in a non-stop stream'.

Prince Andrew, then four, wanted to give his little brother a well-worn teddy bear but when he was told it was too big, he took it to bed himself.

It was six weeks after the birth before the baby's name was revealed – Edward Antony Richard Louis.

Edward and Richard were former kings; Louis was in honour of Earl (Louis) Mountbatten – Prince Philip's favourite uncle, while Antony, which had never been used before in the royal family, was a compliment to Princess Margaret's then husband, Antony Armstrong-Jones.

Edward was christened on June 12, when he was 14 weeks old.

IN THE NEWS:
Britain's 7,000-strong peace force was struggling to maintain order in Cyprus as fighting escalated between Greek and Turkish Cypriots

Jack Ruby was being tried for the murder of Lee Harvey Oswald

ON THE BOX:
Big Night Out with Mike and Bernie Winters

TOP OF THE CHARTS:
Anyone Who Had A Heart, Cilla Black

A special guest at Trooping the Colour, June 1964

The Queen, Andrew and baby Edward in his crib, June 1964

A relaxed stroll in Windsor on the Queen's 39th birthday, April 1965

Andrew fetches a flower...

...which Anne lifts above Edward's head

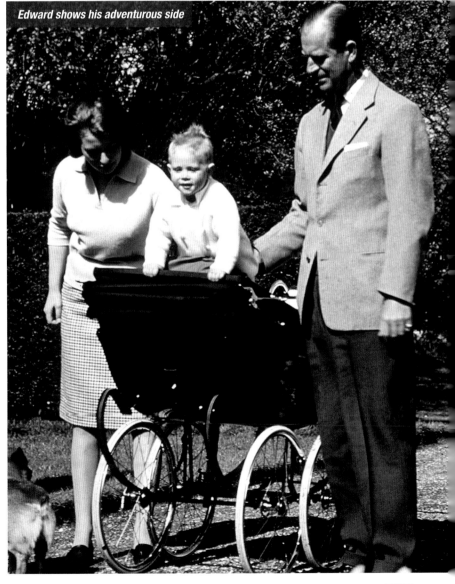

Edward shows his adventurous side

The day they were born

HARRY, 15.09.1984

The second child of Prince Charles and Princess Diana broke with royal tradition in that he was named almost immediately.

Henry Charles Albert David – to be known as Prince Harry – was five days late when he eventually arrived at St Mary's Hospital, Paddington.

Of course, Henry has strong royal connotations, given it has been the name for eight kings. Charles came from Harry's father and Diana's brother. Albert, also common in the Spencer family, was the name of King George VI and Queen Victoria's husband, while David was the name of the Queen Mother's brother, David Bowes-Lyon.

Diana had been driven to hospital at 7.30am on September 15, with the birth finally happening at 4.20pm. It was a smooth and trouble-free labour.

The Queen was telephoned in Balmoral by Charles less than half an hour after Harry's arrival to be given the good news.

After one night in hospital, Diana, Harry and Charles left the hospital together at 2.30pm the following day.

After dropping them off at Kensington Palace, where Prince William was waiting, Charles picked up his polo gear and headed out to Windsor for a match, where he scored a hat-trick.

As for William, apparently his excited squeals woke up his baby brother.

Harry was christened at Windsor Castle on December 27.

IN THE NEWS:
The miner's strike was into its 27th week and a settlement seemed a long way off as peace talks between the National Coal Board and NUM collapsed

ON THE BOX:
The A-Team
The Paul Daniels Magic Show
Dynasty

TOP OF THE CHARTS:
I Just Called To Say I Love You, Stevie Wonder

Leaving hospital, September 1984

Diana peers at her new son on the steps of St Mary's Hospital

A family portrait at Harry's christening, December 1984

Family snaps

Top:
Diana, Harry, William and Charles, 1985

Middle:
Charles holds Harry during the Trooping the Colour ceremony, June 1985

Left:
Mum and son, July 1985

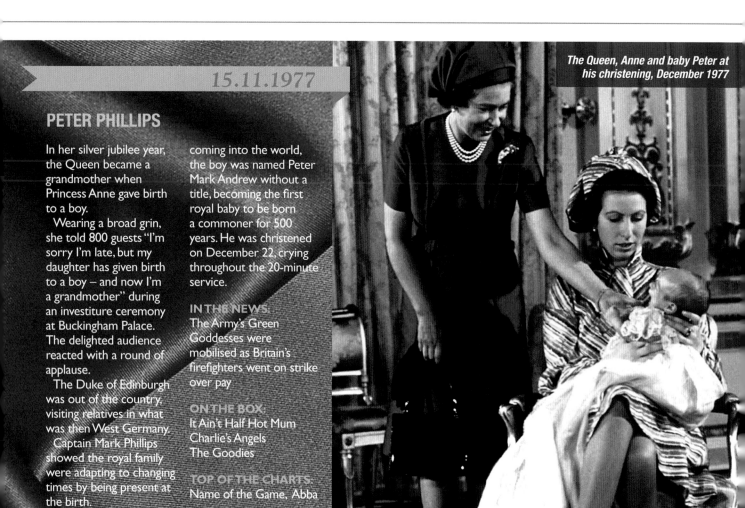

15.11.1977

The Queen, Anne and baby Peter at his christening, December 1977

PETER PHILLIPS

In her silver jubilee year, the Queen became a grandmother when Princess Anne gave birth to a boy.

Wearing a broad grin, she told 800 guests "I'm sorry I'm late, but my daughter has given birth to a boy – and now I'm a grandmother" during an investiture ceremony at Buckingham Palace. The delighted audience reacted with a round of applause.

The Duke of Edinburgh was out of the country, visiting relatives in what was then West Germany.

Captain Mark Phillips showed the royal family were adapting to changing times by being present at the birth.

Almost a month after coming into the world, the boy was named Peter Mark Andrew without a title, becoming the first royal baby to be born a commoner for 500 years. He was christened on December 22, crying throughout the 20-minute service.

IN THE NEWS:
The Army's Green Goddesses were mobilised as Britain's firefighters went on strike over pay

ON THE BOX:
It Ain't Half Hot Mum
Charlie's Angels
The Goodies

TOP OF THE CHARTS:
Name of the Game, Abba

Zara with big brother, November 1982

15.05.1981

ZARA PHILLIPS

Princess Anne's second child was a girl weighing 8lb 10oz, arriving just six hours after she was driven to St Mary's Hospital in Paddington by her private detective.

After the "perfectly normal" delivery, Anne was said to have joked: "Right, Mark and I have done our bit. Now it's up to Charles and Diana (who were due to marry two months later)."

It was almost four weeks before the girl was named – Zara Anne Elizabeth. A Buckingham Palace spokesman said: "Princess Anne and Captain Phillips just liked the name. They don't know anyone called Zara, and she is not named after anyone." Like her brother, Peter, Zara was not given a royal title.

IN THE NEWS:
The Pope was recovering from major surgery after he was shot four times in St Peter's Square, Vatican City

Tottenham won a thrilling FA Cup final replay, defeating Manchester City 3-2 thanks to Ricky Villa's brilliant winning goal

ON THE BOX:
The Professionals
Knots Landing

TOP OF THE CHARTS:
Stand And Deliver, Adam Ant

08.08.88

BEATRICE

The Duke and Duchess of York celebrated their first child when a girl was born on the eighth day of the eighth month in 1988.

Prince Andrew drove his wife to London's Portland Hospital, arriving at 9.55am, and it was 8.18pm that evening when his daughter came into the world following an induced birth. There were no complications.

Just 48 hours before, the Duke had flown home from Singapore, where he had been serving on HMS Edinburgh. The day before the birth, he had taken Fergie for a spin in her open-topped Jaguar XJS.

Mum and daughter left hospital four days after the birth – and immediately became the youngest royal to fly as she jetted to Scotland to spend time with the Queen at Balmoral.

She was named Beatrice Elizabeth Mary when she was two weeks old and christened shortly before Christmas.

IN THE NEWS:
A search for the body of Moors murder victim Keith Bennett was ongoing

ON THE BOX:
Ever Decreasing Circles
Rough Guide to Europe

TOP OF THE CHARTS:
The Only Way Is Up, Yazz and the Plastic Population

An official portrait at Balmoral when Beatrice was two weeks old

23.03.1990

The royal family leave the church after Eugenie's christening

EUGENIE

A little over 18 months after Beatrice's birth, the Duchess of York gave birth to another girl, with a caesarean section required after the baby, facing the wrong way, became distressed.

The girl, weighing 7lb 2oz, was born at 7.58pm, less than four hours after Fergie had arrived at hospital.

She had gone into labour naturally, despite planning to be induced the following day.

The baby left hospital a week after the birth, and on the same day was named Eugenie Victoria Helena.

Eugenie was a granddaughter of Queen Victoria; Victoria speaks for itself and Helena was the name of Queen Victoria's third daughter.

IN THE NEWS:
Labour won a landslide victory in the Mid-Staffordshire by-election, with the Tories losing thousands of votes because of anger at the poll tax

ON THE BOX:
A Bit of Fry and Laurie
Cheers
Surprise! Surprise!

TOP OF THE CHARTS:
Dub Be Good To Me, Beats International and Lindy Layton

MORE BABY MEMORIES

Covering the last 75 years, here are a selection of images of more royal babies, including the children of Princess Margaret, the Duchess of Kent and Prince Edward

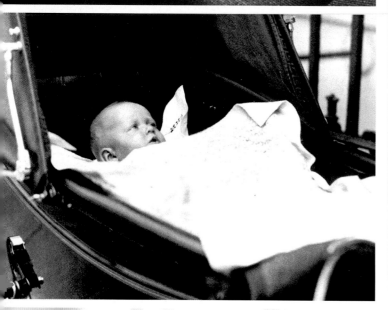

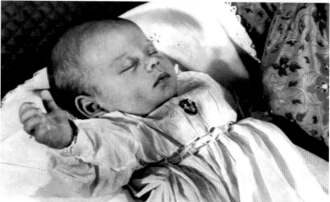

Pleased to meet you

Clockwise:
Princess Alexandra in her pram, 1937

Princess Margaret cuddles baby son Viscount Linley, December 1961

Lady Helen Windsor, June 1964

A look of love from the Duchess of Kent as she holds her first child, the Earl of St Andrews, July 1962. To the left, the Earl is shown enjoying the sun on his first birthday

The look of love

Clockwise:
The Kent family in September 1970,
admiring baby Nicholas Windsor

Lord Frederick Windsor's christening,
July 1979

The Earl and Countess of Wessex leaving
Frimley Park Hospital with their first
child, Lady Louise, who was born after an
emergency caesarean, November 2003

Autumn Phillips, Peter's wife, with their
first child, Savannah, August 2011

Edward holds his and Sophie's second
child, James, Viscount Severn, 2007

Grandad Michael

Great Granny & Great Grandfather

Step-Granny Camilla

Uncle James

Granny Carole

Grandad Charles

Auntie Pippa

Meet

THE FAMILY

The latest heir to the throne will receive plenty of love, care and attention from the Windsors and Middletons

THE arrival of the royal baby won't just be a life-changer for **William and Kate**. Their immediate family are also about to take on new roles and responsibilities.

At the age of 64, Charles becomes a grandfather for the first time and in the days after the pregnancy was announced, he spoke of how much he was relishing the prospect.

"I'm thrilled, marvellous," he said. "It's a lovely thought and I look forward enormously to that relationship. It's a very nice thought to become a grandfather in my old age, if I can say so."

Charles is already a step-grandfather through his wife Camilla's five grandchildren. It has been claimed that he doesn't always welcome the attention of "little people" at his Highgrove residence, as he finds it difficult to relax when they are charging about.

Uncle Harry

FAMILY TREE

Prince of Cambridge
22 July 2013

Catherine Middleton
09 January 1982

Prince William
21 June 1982

Prince Harry
1984

Pippa Middleton
1983

James Middleton
1987

Michael Middleton
1949

Carole Goldsmith
1955

Anne 1950	**Andrew** 1960	**Edward** 1964

Prince Charles
1948

Diana Spencer
1961 – died 1997

Camilla
1947

Peter Middleton
1920 – died 2010

Valerie Glassborrow
1924 – died 2006

Queen Elizabeth II
1926

Prince Phillip
1921

Richard Middleton
1878 – died 1951

Olive Lupton
1881 – died 1936

Edward VIII
1894 – died 1972
(Abdicated the throne in 1936
to marry Wallis Simpson)

George VI
1895 – died 1952

Lady Elizabeth Bowes-Lyon
1900 – died 2002

John Middleton
1839 – died 1887

Mary Asquith
1839 – died 1889

George V
1865 – died 1936

Princess Mary of Teck
1867 – died 1953

William Middleton
1807 – died 1884

Mary Ward
1811 – died 1859

King Edward VII
1841 – died 1910

Princess Alexandra
1844 – died 1925

Great Uncle Andrew

It will be interesting to see if he is more accommodating when it is his own grandchild causing a commotion.

For the Queen and Duke of Edinburgh, this is their third great-grandchild, as Princess Anne's eldest son Peter Phillips is the father to two daughters with his Canadian wife, Autumn.

The Queen and Philip are very fond of William and Kate and are sure to see a lot of the new addition to the family and take a particular interest in his upbringing, given he will one day succeed to the throne.

Princes Andrew and Edward, and Anne, the Princess Royal, are likely to have more of a background role, but can certainly offer plenty of advice given they are all parents to two children.

Prince Harry, approaching his 29th birthday, becomes an uncle for the first time, and royal observers will be watching to see how he will approach the role, given his propensity for laddish behaviour.

Shortly after the pregnancy became public knowledge, Harry, who was serving with the Army in Helmand Province, Afghanistan, said: "Obviously I'm thrilled for both of them. It's about time, I can't wait to be an uncle."

We wait to see if he will be entrusted with the role of godparent alongside Auntie Pippa. Their prominence in the wedding (best man and chief bridesmaid) make them favourites.

Victoria Arbiter, a royal contributor for ABC News in America, is looking forward to seeing how William and Kate's siblings build a relationship with their new nephew. She commented: "Everybody needs an Uncle Harry and an Aunt Pippa in their lives. You've got stylish Pippa and great, fun Uncle Harry so I think they're going to be wonderful people to have around. You can imagine it's going to be great fun.

"Kate is very close to her sister, Pippa, and William is infinitely, in the same way, close to Prince Harry. So, they are the obvious choice [as godparents]. They were the best man and the chief bridesmaid at their wedding, they're well-trusted, they're family.

"Harry covers the royal side, Pippa covers the Middleton side. So, of course it's very early days to be thinking about that stuff, but they're probably a shoo-in."

Neither Harry or Pippa appear in any rush to settle down and have children of their own. It will be intriguing to monitor whether their close access to the baby will have any effect on them and change their outlook on life as they approach their thirties.

A new role is also in store for Carole and Michael Middleton, as Kate's parents celebrate the arrival of their first grandchild.

They are said to be thrilled and ultra-keen to help out as much as they can, which is excellent news for William and Kate who want to keep care of the baby in the family as much as possible.

At one stage it was thought that the new prince would spend the first six weeks of his life living at the Middletons' £4.85m mansion in Buckleberry, Berkshire, as the 21-room apartment within Kensington Palace earmarked for the Cambridges was being refurbished.

However, they have decided to live within a smaller apartment at the Palace while they wait for work on their new home to be completed. The refurbishment of the large block proved problematic because asbestos was discovered and had to be eradicated before anyone could move in.

Even though they won't be sharing accommodation, the Middletons will be close at hand during the early stages of parenthood. Carole, the mother of three children, can offer advice and support based on years of experience, especially when William has to return to work as a helicopter pilot in Anglesey once his paternity leave is over.

Given that William is known to admire the closeness of the Middletons, he will feel more relaxed about his wife and baby having such loving assistance while he is away.

Carole has enjoyed overseeing the redecoration of their own house, bought in 2012, including the installation of a new kitchen and nursery-style room.

After he was born, William lived with his parents in Kensington Palace. Diana employed a nurse to help her in the first few weeks before a nanny moved in. Kate doesn't feel in need of outside assistance at this stage, although it should be noted that Diana hadn't quite reached her 21st birthday when she became a mother, while the Duchess is 31.

William and Kate were hoping to move into their apartment in early autumn 2013, but wherever they live, the most prominent royal couple – and their new addition – can be certain to receive plenty of love and support from their immediate families as they face all the challenges that lie ahead. ■

Great Uncle Edward

Great Auntie Anne

NEXT IN Line

They may face a long wait but the new addition to the family will one day take the crown

WILLIAM and Kate's son has immediately taken up third position in the royal line of succession, behind his grandfather and father.

All being well the new prince is unlikely to take the crown for a long time but they probably won't have to be as patient as the Prince of Wales.

Charles has waited longer than anyone else in history to ascend the throne, having been next in line since King George VI's death in 1952 when he was just three years old.

The previous record holder was Edward VII who succeeded Queen Victoria in 1901 after a wait of 59 years, two months and 13 days. Charles passed that mark in April 2011.

So far the Queen has resisted any suggestion that she abdicate to allow her eldest son to take over, with her reign now extended past 61 years, just two years shy of the longest-reigning monarch, Queen Victoria.

There has been a recent precedent in the Netherlands where in April 75-year-old Queen Beatrix abdicated and son Prince Willem-Alexander became king.

Although they won't directly affect Charles and William's eventual succession, changes are afoot to the royal line as the Succession To The Crown Act was passed by parliament in April 2013.

The main consequence of the Act, which for many was long overdue, is to end the principle of sons taking precedence over daughters as heirs to the throne. It also lifts the bar on the sovereign and prospective heirs from

Queen Victoria (top), the longest-reigning monarch, and Edward VII, who waited nearly 60 years to succeed her

marrying a Catholic.

The basis for the succession was determined in the 17th century, via the Bill of Rights (1689) and the Act of Settlement (1701). Under the Act of Settlement, women were superseded by their brothers in succession even if they were the first born.

The changes apply retrospectively so a child born after 28 October 2011 will be subject to the new rules, removing any gender preference from the laws of succession.

The current prohibition on the monarch being a Catholic will remain in force, but members of the royal family who marry a Catholic will no longer lose their place in line to the throne.

The Act of Settlement bestowed succession on Protestant descendants of Princess Sophia – the Electress of Hanover and granddaughter of James I. Subsequent acts have confirmed this.

Those in the line of succession are eligible to succeed to the throne of the United Kingdom and the other 15 Commonwealth realms.

The sovereign must be in communion with the Church of England and must swear to preserve the established Church of England and the established Church of Scotland. The sovereign must also promise to uphold the Protestant succession.

The line of succession updates as a result of events, such as births, deaths or marriages. Any further children born in wedlock to the Duke of Cambridge will immediately follow older siblings in the list, while preceding everyone below.

The line of succession

SOVEREIGN

1. The Prince of Wales
2. The Duke of Cambridge
3. The Prince of Cambridge
4. Prince Henry of Wales
5. The Duke of York
6. Princess Beatrice of York
7. Princess Eugenie of York
8. The Earl of Wessex
9. Viscount Severn
10. The Lady Louise Mountbatten-Windsor
11. The Princess Royal
12. Mr Peter Phillips
13. Miss Savannah Phillips
14. Miss Isla Phillips
15. Mrs Michael Tindall
16. Viscount Linley
17. The Hon. Charles Armstrong-Jones
18. The Hon. Margarita Armstrong-Jones
19. The Lady Sarah Chatto
20. Mr Samuel Chatto
21. Mr Arthur Chatto
22. The Duke of Gloucester
23. Earl of Ulster
24. Lord Culloden
25. The Lady Cosima Windsor
26. The Lady Davina Lewis
27. Master Tane Lewis
28. Miss Senna Lewis
29. The Lady Rose Gilman
30. Master Rufus Gilman
31. Miss Lyla Gilman
32. The Duke of Kent
33. The Lady Amelia Windsor
34. The Lady Helen Taylor
35. Mr Columbus Taylor
36. Mr Cassius Taylor
37. Miss Eloise Taylor
38. Miss Estella Taylor
39. The Hon. Albert Windsor
40. The Hon. Leopold Windsor

Taken from www.royal.gov.uk

Congratulations

PRINCE CHARLES:

"Both my wife and I are overjoyed at the arrival of my first grandchild. It is an incredibly special moment for William and Catherine and we are so thrilled for them on the birth of their baby boy.

"Grandparenthood is a unique moment in anyone's life, as countless kind people have told me in recent months, so I am enormously proud and happy to be a grandfather for the first time and we are eagerly looking forward to seeing the baby in the near future."

DAVID CAMERON:

"It is wonderful news from St Mary's Paddington, and I am sure right across the country and right across the Commonwealth people will be celebrating and wishing the royal couple well. It is an important moment in the life of our nation, but I suppose above all it is an important moment for a warm and loving couple who have got a brand new baby boy.

Following the birth of the new prince, joyful messages and best wishes were sent from all over the globe . . .

"Miriam and I want to congratulate The Duke and Duchess of Cambridge on the birth of their son. This is wonderful news which will make the whole country smile.

"The arrival of a first child is a very special time and we send our very best wishes to The Duke and Duchess of Cambridge - and indeed to all couples who have become proud parents on this very special day."

LABOUR LEADER ED MILIBAND:
"Many congratulations to the Duke and Duchess of Cambridge. I wish them and their son all happiness and good health."

SCOTTISH FIRST MINISTER ALEX SALMOND:
"I am sure that people across Scotland will be absolutely thrilled to hear the news of the birth of a baby boy to the royal couple and will want to join me in wishing the proud parents many congratulations."

WELSH FIRST MINISTER CARWYN JONES:
"On behalf of the people of Wales, I would like to congratulate the Duke and Duchess of Cambridge on the birth of their baby boy.

"The couple already have established and strong links with Wales, choosing Anglesey to start their married life, and they will always have a very warm welcome home here as a family.

"I would like to wish the Duke and Duchess all the very best as they enter their journey into parenthood."

What they said...

CHERYL COLE:
"Congratulations to William and Kate!! So happy they have a healthy baby and everyone is good. Can't wait to see him now. #Royalbaby."

OPERA SINGER KATHERINE JENKINS:
"Awwww... It's a boy! Congratulations! Sooo happy for you! #GlassesRaised #Toast #Celebrations"

The London Eye glows a patriotic red, white and blue in honour of the new prince

US PRESIDENT BARACK OBAMA:

"Michelle and I are so pleased to congratulate the Duke and Duchess of Cambridge on the joyous occasion of the birth of their first child.

"We wish them all the happiness and blessings parenthood brings. The child enters the world at a time of promise and opportunity for our two nations.

"Given the special relationship between us, the American people are pleased to join with the people of the United Kingdom as they celebrate the birth of the young prince."

AUSTRALIAN PRIME MINISTER KEVIN RUDD:

"I think all Australians at the bottom of their hearts wish the royal bub all the best, and certainly wish the new parents all the best as well. This is a day of great joy.

"To Prince Charles and Camilla, they have the delight of being grandparents, all I can say is, this is probably one of the best experiences of your life. And I'm sure they're going to have a wonderful time with the royal baby. And Her Majesty the Queen and to the Duke of Edinburgh, the special delight of a great-grandchild. So, on behalf of all Australians, we wish the family all the best at this wonderful time of celebration."

RUSSIAN PRESIDENT VLADIMIR PUTIN:

"Russian President Vladimir Putin has congratulated Queen Elizabeth II of the United Kingdom of Great Britain and Northern Ireland on the birth of her great-grandson. He wished the newborn baby, the Duchess of Cambridge and all members of the Royal Family good health."

What they said...

AMERICAN COMEDIENNE JOAN RIVERS:

"Congratulations to Kate & William on the birth of their baby boy! So relieved that his name won't include the words Ivy or Apple."

STEPHEN FRY:

"The official easel. We really are a marvellously bonkers country."

The Royal Birth in Numbers

8.6

The royal baby, weighing in at 8lb 6oz, is larger than average, and the heaviest future king at birth for at least 100 years (in the past, birth weights of monarchs were not revealed).

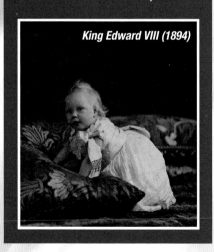

King Edward VIII (1894)

Prince William weighed 7lb 1.5oz, while Prince Charles was 7lb 6oz. The baby is not the heaviest royal, though – Savannah Phillips, the Queen's first great-grandchild, weighed 8lb 8oz when she was born in December 2010.

7.8

The baby's weight was above the national average – 7lb 8oz for boys and 7lb 4oz for girls.

22.06.82

Prince William was unveiled to the world on the very same steps as his son at St. Mary's Hospital in London on June 22, 1982 by his parents Prince Charles and Princess Diana. His mum was wearing a polka dot dress like Kate.

65%

As a 31-year-old father, Prince William is far from unusual - 65% of babies are born to dads who are over 30.

2,200

In 2013 approximately 2,200 babies are born each day in the United Kingdom, which is higher than at any time since 1971.

22.07

The Royal Mint will give babies born on the same day (July 22) as the new prince a special silver penny to mark the occasion. A total of 2,013 of the coins have been minted and parents were given 60 days after the birth to claim the special present, which will come in a pink or blue pouch depending on the sex of the baby.

30.7

As a 31-year-old mother, the Duchess of Cambridge reflects the average for a married woman having her first baby (30.7). Among unmarried mothers, the average is 27.6.

'It's very emotional. It's such a special time. I think any parent will know what this feeling feels like'

– Kate